'In the interpretation of vital  than the cell as revealed constitute a super-structure g chemical forces. The univ science are in accordance wi *ultimate atomic divisibility of* *not by the cell.'*

Dr Albert Abrams, 1916

Electrohealing

The Medicine of the Future

Roger Coghill

Thorsons
An Imprint of HarperCollins*Publishers*

Thorsons
An Imprint of HarperCollins*Publishers*
77–85 Fulham Palace Road,
Hammersmith, London W6 8JB

Published by Thorsons 1992
10 9 8 7 6 5 4 3 2 1

© Roger Coghill 1992

Roger Coghill asserts the moral right to
be identified as the author of this work

A catalogue record for this book
is available from the British Library

ISBN 0 7225 2559 1

Typeset by Harper Phototypesetters Limited,
Northampton, England
Printed in Great Britain by
Billings Bookplan Ltd, Worcester

Contents

For my son, Thomas, who will see tomorrow's world.

Acknowledgements

This has been a lonely book to write. Throughout its compilation it seemed as if I was drawing information from folk so different in outlook, discipline, and belief that to have seated them round one dinner table would have been an act of social folly.

Yet the ultimate purpose of this work is to unify, not to divide: to bring together the cats and the dogs of complementary and conventional medicine, to mediate between the categorical denial and the dogmatic pronouncement.

So I will simply list here, in alphabetical order, some of those people who have directly or indirectly had a formative influence on this volume: Mike and Jenny Adams, Robert Becker, Valerie Beral, Simon Best, Sue Black, Vivien Brown, Antonia Carr, Richard Dixey, Peter Duesberg, Marylin Ferguson, Clare Francis, Herbert Frolich, Richard Gerber, Jean Golding, John Gribbin, Samuel Hahnemann, John Hardaker, Julian Kenyon, Mary Lawrence, Valeri Lednev, Lizzie my dog, Dan Lyle, John Male, Neil Mayhew, Alisdair Philips, Ilse Pope, Pythagoras of Samos, Thomas Saunders, Erwin Schrodinger, Rupert Sheldrake, Cyril Smith, Ric Tell, James D. Watson, and Bary and Mark Wilson. Some of them will never know why.

I also acknowledge with grateful thanks permission from many publishers to quote what I believe to be important statements from books already in print. I hope that the more elegant ways than I was capable of by which their authors have been able to express new concepts and insights, which I have duly acknowledged in the text, will encourage my readers to seek out these works for their further understanding.

Roger Coghill
Funchal, Madeira, 1991.

Foreword

Roger Coghill is no stranger to controversy and bold statement. His on-going research on the health effects of electromagnetic fields (EMFs) have made him an outspoken critic of current UK guidelines for public exposure to sources of man-made EMFs and he has given evidence at a number of public enquiries into the siting of powerlines and radar.

But in this book he turns his focus on the healing power of EMFs and, in tracing the history and development of electrohealing, offers the reader some challenging ideas on how the body and brain may use EMFs to maintain health and initiate the body's healing mechanisms. His theory of cerebral morphogenetic radiation and how it may mediate these processes is both innovative and capable of being experimentally tested and validated. Likewise, his discussion of the ideas of the early pioneers of electrohealing and how many were rejected, suppressed or denigrated by the medical and scientific authorities and vested interests of the time, is both instructive and a warning to those trying to promote this field today.

In particular, the neglected technique, pioneered in the 1930s in the United States, of haemo-irradiation, whereby a patient's blood is irradiated with ultraviolet light and then replaced, is examined with details of case histories. From the remarkable number and variety of cases in which the treatment cured the ailment or strongly alleviated the symptoms, and in the light of what we now know about the biological effects of electromagnetism, a modern, controlled study of haemo-irradiation seems long overdue. Whatever the result, this book is a timely and stimulating presentation of the beneficial use of electromagnetism in healing, a technique that promises to become one of the cornerstones of 21st century medicine.

Simon Best

Simon Best is co-author of the prize winning book *Electromagnetic Man* and editor of *Electromagnetic News* based at PO Box 25, Liphook, Hants GU30 7SE, England.

Introduction:
Towards Electromedicine

The brain minds the body. This idea seems so simple and central to the understanding of human health, and yet it has escaped the attention of the mainstream of medical practice and psychological thought.

Robert Ornstein and David Sobel, *The Healing Brain*, 1987.

During this book I hope to move us all a little closer to understanding the organic healing process which so intrigued Erwin Schrodinger, the physicist. This understanding may leave much still mysterious, but a pathway at least has been cleared, mainly through research in the last decade, for the emergence of the electromedicine of the twenty-first century, and for our more careful exposure criteria against non-ionizing radiation, so skilfully and prodigally exploited during the twentieth.

We can divide electrohealing's contribution to organic health into seven categories:

a) Protection: using Faradic protection or other avoidance techniques to create a safe space where no foreign EM fields can intrude to debilitate the organism's repair operations.

b) Diagnosis: using the body's own ultraweak emissions of electromagnetic energy to find out what is going wrong within.

c) Neutralizing: using the heterodyne principle to cancel out electromagnetic interference not useful to the healing process or the processes of growth control.

d) Direct current applications: where natural injury currents, both in bone and soft tissue, can be assisted to speed up the healing process.

e) Direct and alternating magnetic fields: for degaussing magnetized cells, or cells whose polarities are in disarray.
f) Pulsed EM fields: for helping the brain's message to carry deep into the body's confines and improving signal quality for protein synthesis and DNA uncoiling.
g) Phototherapy: using light or near light frequencies to heal dermal and epidermal complaints, and also for restoring melatonin-serotonin cycles to normal.

The techniques opened up by Abrams and Boyd, and continuing via radionics to the modern use of Vega and similar diagnostic machines, are still lacking a vital component: our understanding of how such techniques actually work – if they do work that is, which is still far from proven by modern research.

Given the glimmerings of insight provided by Becker, Marino, Frey, Adey, Blackman, Liboff, Goodman, Liburdy and others in the United States, and Gulayev, Kholodov, Karu, among others in Russia, and the work of Bellosi, del Guidice, Conti, and their fellows in Italy, we have come a long way. Our understanding of how the organic cell might be instructed by specific electromagnetic signals (and conversely how those signals might be disrupted or inhibited by the wrong frequencies or wavelengths) has advanced to the point where a prize as great as that secured by Crick and Watson in the unravelling of the DNA macromolecular structure is within our grasp. Ultimately we shall be able to decode those signals from the brain and correlate them with the specific material structures of DNA.

How much progress have we really made in that direction, though, when the final insight and acceptance is still lacking among the general medical community? When the chasm between complementary and conventional medicine still yawns, with fault on both sides? They have much to offer each other, yet little exchange seems to be taking place, not so much through antagonism as the sheer lack of a firmly-based mechanism for some of the practices of both sides.

More specifically, though Wilder Penfield first mapped the motor and sensory control areas in the cortex in the 1930s, thereby uncovering one of the great clues to cerebral morphogenetic fields, the task ahead still remains to trace the precise nature of those inter-hemispheral ion flows through the corpus callosum, and convert them into intelligible coherent digital form.

At least at that level we may then discern crude differences in signal characteristics. These in turn might allow us to generate for ourselves those basic signals which are specific to the organ being instructed for protein synthesis or other mitotic processes in the cell cycle. Even after that the detailed EM signals will probably be too highly complex and ordered at such minute intensities for our current instruments to follow in detail.

But just as we do not need to know the exact repositionings of charge which have occurred in the magnetic audio tape on which we have just recorded our favourite tune from some radio transmission, so it may not be necessary – except at a quantum theoretical level – to reach down to that detail. The concepts behind acupuncture suggest it is enough simply to unblock obstructions to these unique signals (the Chinese would call them Ch'i) rather than to attempt any precise amplification and retransmission.

Although the authorities have been slow to acknowledge either the contributions of complementary medicine or the possibility that organic life is sensitive to extremely weak electromagnetic influences not strong enough to induce any thermal effects, their position has to change.

First, the emerging research picture cannot any longer be denied: in the United States the first concerns were expressed officially as far back as 1971. In the last few years, the Congressional Office of Technology Assessment, and then the Environmental Protection Agency, and even the Federal Drug Administration has shown distinct signs of a changed, more accommodating position. In China and Russia large-scale epidemiological surveys have been carried out leaving little doubt that what test-tube studies have been saying for years, and what cellular biologists have been quantifying, are not without substance.

There is also supporting evidence for electromagnetic bio-effects from some quite unexpected sources: from palaeontology, and even from Greek philosophy and legend, for example, and they all seem to be saying effectively that our time for adequate response is quickly evaporating. Among palaeontologists it is well established that from time to time the earth's magnetic field has reversed its polarity. No one has any idea why, and it is only now becoming clear that such occasions may be accompanied by mass extinctions of species on a large scale. And that the reversals themselves occur in a relatively short timespan.

It was suggested by R. J. Uffen in 1963 that at the time of magnetic reversal there would be a dramatic increase in ionizing radiation at the earth's surface as the earth's magnetic field strength passed through zero. That position is now regarded as unlikely, but only a year later Harrison and Funnel found that a certain species of tiny marine animal, radiolaria, underwent mass extinction at the same time as the reversal, and similar mass extinctions have since been likewise associated, chiefly through the work of Hays at the Lamont Dogherty Geological Observatory.

Commenting on these discoveries, Robert Becker makes the chilling observation that:

The distribution of these species was widespread, and the extinctions occurred within a relatively short space of time, and were not preceded by a period of declining population. In fact in some instances the population seemed to be approaching a maximum before the abrupt extinction occurred.

With a current human population of some 6,000 million doubling every thirteen years and unlikely to be self-sustaining for much longer, we could be said to be in a similar position, particularly against a background of fast-thinning ozone protection with little really adequate response by authorities.

From a completely different standpoint, it may be no more than coincidence, but Plato in his *Timaeus* and *Critias* works, causes the Egyptian priest at Sais to make some remarkable statements. Having asserted the superiority of his priesthood for its care in preserving ancient records for periods much earlier than the Greeks, he answers Solon thus:

You are all young in mind you have no belief rooted in old tradition and no knowledge hoary with age. And the reason is this. There have been and will be many different calamities to destroy mankind, the greatest of them by fire and water, lesser ones by countless other means.

Your own story of how Phaethon, child of the sun, harnessed his father's chariot but was unable to guide it along his father's course, so burnt up things on the earth and was himself destroyed by a thunderbolt, is a mythical version of the truth that there is at long intervals a variation in the course of the heavenly bodies and a consequent widespread destruction by fire of things on the earth. When on the other hand the gods purge the earth with a deluge, the herdsmen and the shepherds in the mountains escape, but those living in the cities in your part of the world are swept into the sea by the rivers . . . so that you have to begin again like children, in complete ignorance of what happened in our part of the world or yours in early times.

One effect of the earth's magnetic field reversal on its organic life concerns the intimate nature of how organic chemical molecules are bonded together. As Becker and Marino explain:

All such organic chemicals, exist in two forms, identical in composition and in the arrangement of components, except sterically, where there are always two isomeric forms. These are revealed through their ability to rotate light transmitted through their solutions. There are dextrorotatory (D) forms and laevorotatory (L) forms. All artificial procedures for producing these chemicals, including Miller's technique and its derivatives, produce a mixture of both forms in roughly equal amounts. Living things on the other hand are always composed of one type: dependent on the species, all organic chemicals within their bodies will either be D or L forms, but never both. To arrive at the same result artificially one must deliberately start with chemicals of all one structural type or introduce the symmetry in some other fashion.

Similarly, the magnetic fields emanating from a bar magnetic are circularly or rather helically emitted: those emanating from the north pole are laevoratory and those from the south pole dextrorotatory. Should these in any way be responsible or influence the construction of organic molecules, then a complete reversal of the earth's field may also have profound and swift biological repercussions.

Negative ions will all be spinning in one direction, and positive ions in the other relative to any structure. In considering the DNA macromolecule, not only is it polarized, but it is helically constructed, so that an electron with the correct spin would pass down its centre easily from H-bond to H-bond from one end to the other, whereas a positive ion, spinning in the opposite direction would find the journey difficult if not impossible.

The conventional bar magnet illustrates how negative ions spin from one pole (see figure 8.1). The north pole spins counter clockwise (to the left) and is laevorotatory, while the south pole spins clockwise (to the right) and is dextrorotatory. This may be why negative ions appear to be beneficial to the healing process in our bodies, whose cells are constructed to be laevorotatory.

The curious earthworm reaction to the south pole of a magnet reported by Dr Roy Davis in 1936 (see page 55) seems to show that these creatures, which are incredibly sensitive to UV light, do not like the influence of dextrorotating fields, and, as he found, continually try to escape from any adjacently placed containers, by eating their way out. Even so they died.

In tracing one mass extinction, palaeontologists found the bones of many differing species huddled together – predator and prey alike – in the deepest recesses of caves. The bones were in no way mutilated, as they would have been if one species had been eating the other and left its remains within. The mystery for them was, what had caused these normally incompatible creatures to flee the sunlight into darkness? Could it have been radiation?

We know of periods in which mass extinction of a number of species, composed of many individuals, happened. In the first, at the end of the Permian period, nearly half the species of animals then in existence – ranging from protozoans to terrestrial tetrapods – no longer survived. The second, at the end of the Cretaceous period, showed the same phenomenon: a great number of different species became extinct including the dinosaurs, and the marine and flying reptiles.

As Becker astutely points out:

In both instances the events coincided with the re-establishment of frequent magnetic field reversals, following a long quiescent interval. The field reversal therefore seems to represent an evolutionary selective process of great importance.

It is also of great importance because the last reversal happened 5,000 years ago, and another is well overdue. Already we may be influencing that event: today, one in four of the human species in developed countries are dying of cancer, many of them prematurely. Though in the great scheme of things our efforts may prove vain as the enormous forces of the universe enact their timeless balletic drama, we, blinkered by our microscopic views and the minutiae of individual human *Sturm und Drang*, can perhaps do no more than arrest our final fatal destiny for a moment or two, like some small flotsam on the ocean's wave pauses before being cast onto an immense shore.

If we do no more than comprehend the magnificence of the universe, the parsimony of each single organic cell, and the way the two – so phenomenally different in volume and mechanism – are but one connected whole, connected at an electronic level – we will have achieved a worthwhile objective. If at that time we can also learn the secrets of our planet's wholeness and health, we will have done even better.

1. The Healing Brain

How would we express in terms of statistical theory the marvellous faculty of an organism, by which it delays its decay into thermodynamical equilibrium (death)?

Erwin Schrodinger, *What is Life?* (1944)

Human beings are more than just collections of individual cells. In 1670 Robert Hooke peered with amazement down Van Leuwenhook's newly-invented microscope to discover for the first time what every schoolchild now learns in elementary biology lessons: that we, and all other creatures on this planet, are entirely created out of myriads of individual cells and the fluids which flow between them.

During the nineteenth century the theory that we humans, complicated though we are, had descended from single cells formed on the shore of some primeval ocean, became accepted. As the jigsaw puzzle of evolution gradually pieced itself together, however, it became obvious that something else, some other factor in the equation of organic life, must be responsible for ordering those impeccable compositions of cells into their functionally different tissues, and maintaining them exactly where they were needed to create a complete, harmonious single organism.

When one thinks about it, that harmony is what we mean by health. For health, just as its original Saxon meaning implies, means being hale or whole. Restoring a body to its whole state, when all its constituent cells are in place and functioning correctly, is what we really mean by healing. Anyone simply thinking of a body as a collection of cells forgets that some organising influence is essential if the cells are to remain where they should be, and repaired when they are damaged.

This book is about that missing ingredient: the control of organic cellular integrity, or morphology, as it is called. It suggests that the missing ingredient is *electromagnetic energy*, the physical force or principle which – unlike any chemical reaction – can cause action to take place at a distance, across the emptiness of space through aqueous liquids, or even in a vacuum. Although interfering with that control process can damage the morphology of any creature, it is a central theme of this book that the application of the correct sort of electromagnetic energy can also restore damaged components.

It seems to be agreed in the main by biologists that during evolution individual solitary cells could sense each other's presence by the chemical reactions within them as they ingested food. Likewise, no physicist would deny that any chemical reaction will cause associated electromagnetic currents. Intracellular reactions inevitably cause electromagnetic fields outside the cell; a nearby cell would therefore know it was in the presence of a neighbour.

Claims by complementary medical practitioners that the universe is one connected whole must be true, if for no other reason than this scientifically accepted phenomenon. Although physicists would unanimously declare that electromagnetic fields weaken (or attenuate) with distance, some of their colleagues, Fritz Albert Popp, Hubert Konig, and Herbert Frolich for instance, have shown that the organic cells of living creatures seem to be able to act like relay stations, amplifying and re-transmitting the ultraweak signals they receive.

As evolution progressed, the solitary cells (unicellular creatures, such as amoebae) somehow began to combine together in groups for efficiency: a group of cells within such combinations could specialize in different tasks, gathering food, say, or helping to move the group along, or look out for predators. This *differentiation* is still evident today: new cells (or *stem cells*) start off as uncharacterized, and then gradually assume a special character, be it as blood cells, skin cells, bone cells or brain cells, all of which perfectly adapted to the role they must play within their organism.

But where is the conductor of such a magnificent biological symphony orchestra? For without such a co-ordinator, the myriads of cells within any multicellular creature would descend once more into disorganized chaos. The chaos which is disease, the chaos which is putrefaction, the chaos which is death.

In 1944 Erwin Schrodinger, one of our most brilliant physicists, discoverer of wave mechanics and a Nobel prizewinner, published some thoughts on this enigma: 'Is life based on the Laws of Physics?' he asked. Having admitted that the science of physics is inescapably a science of statistically large numbers, and not really able to cope with small sets of data, he confessed:

In biology we are faced with an entirely different situation: a single group of atoms existing in only one copy produces orderly events, marvellously tuned in with one another and with the environment according to the most subtle laws. I said, existing only in one copy, for after all we have the example of the egg and of the unicellular organism. In the following stages of a higher organism the copies are multiplied, that is true. But to what extent? Something like 10^{14} in a grown mammal, I understand. What is that! Only a millionth of the number of molecules in one cubic inch of air. Though comparatively bulky, by coalescing they would form but a tiny drop of liquid. And look at the way they are actually distributed. Every cell harbours just one or two of them. Since we know the power this tiny central office has in the isolated cell, do they not resemble stations of local government dispersed through the body, communicating with each other with great ease, thanks to the code that is common to all of them?

It is curious that Schrodinger's book *What is Life?*, which lay, it is said, continuously open on Crick and Watson's laboratory bench as they strove to unravel the structure of DNA, is already using the language of the telecommunications engineer: 'tuned in', 'common code' and so on.

Unwittingly, Schrodinger had already devoted several chapters to the way in which *ionizing electromagnetic radiation* could alter, mutate, or damage the structure of the DNA (or genes as he then knew them), so as to produce confusion – or *entropy* – in the living creature.

What I am proposing is that the essential order necessary for co-ordinating the myriad cells of which we are composed is also instructed by electromagnetic energy, signals emitted centrally; in the case of cerebrate creatures, by their brains. The wrong sort of signals, it seems to me, whether ionizing or not, can damage this vast multicellular partnership, while the right sort can actually promote wholeness or health.

I wrote about the damaging effects of electromagnetic energy in my book *Electropollution* (Thorsons, 1990). Its healing mechanisms, however, are far less well known, and are very much in their infancy. During the chapters which follow we will travel a curious odyssey – from scientific routines widely used in hospitals, to surprising techniques which, though as yet unproven, seem to work where conventional management of the disorder has proved ineffective.

In the animal kingdom there are often examples of creatures which have 'got stuck' and have in consequence stayed at a level of evolution long passed by the others: the coelacanth, for example is typical of the kind of fish inhabiting our planet millions of years ago. The same is true in the cellular world: the single-celled amoeba, and many other unicellular creatures, still live happily and anachronistically among their more evolved multicellular companions.

Of more interest to my story is one of nature's most curious creatures, which offers a clue as to how cells might communicate and co-ordinate their activities. This creature behaves like one single organism: it moves majestically through the waters of its ocean home, catches its food, reaching out long bracts to the particles of organic matter it can sense. Yet this animal is no more than a collection of separate cells which are in no way physically connected to each other. The *Nanomia cara* is known as a siphonophore, an organism carrying a squirting mechanism. It is a close relative of the Portuguese Man of War, which can deliver a powerful sting.

So how does this collection of single cells manage to act in concert? It cannot be by chemical means. The speed of nervous conduction is only 30 metres a second, far too slow to tell the cells what to do. Furthermore, the cells of *Nanomia cara* are not connected in a molecular fashion.

It must presumably be by action at a distance. And that implies electromagnetic communication. That this is so can be shown by putting the poor creature into a bowl of seawater and passing through it an extremely weak electric current. The electromagnetic current then fogs the signals and the 'creature' dissipates into the individual cells of which it is really composed.

Another curious effect happens with certain sea sponges. In 1907, two sponges were put through a sieve, their cells disassociated, and then mixed together. When left in a bowl of seawater for a time the two sponges amazingly separated themselves into their two 'gangs', as if by magic.

In the heart of almost every cell is a *nucleus*; in the nucleus is the now famous deoxyribonucleic acid – DNA – which is unique to every creature on earth.

The police use DNA fingerprinting to distinguish between the cells of two different persons when investigating a crime. Why is the DNA of every creature deliberately different from every other creature?

Could it be so that the multicellular 'gang' can recognize its own signal as distinct from every other creature's signal? In this way the two sets of sponges can separate themselves from each other, even though not physically attached.

The next question to answer before we can properly start our odyssey, is how one can prove that these DNA macro-molecules, which are shaped physically like two spiralling helices, are actually receiving and transmitting signals to each other at a distance? The answer, in a word, is polarity. Even DNA helix has a positively-charged and a negatively-charged end, just like a magnet. In fact many polymers (or chains of molecules) in our bodies are similarly polarized. In the 1960s one researcher (Wildervanck) found out that if he applied an electric field to cells in suspension in a fluid they joined up to make strings or chains, oriented along the lines of magnetic force. When the field was turned off the cells returned to their individual unconnected state.

This clue tells us that cells can feel the presence of electromagnetism at a distance, and perhaps even react to it by moving. The question puzzling scientists is just how such tiny forces can be responsible for large biological effects. This argument is so complicated that I prefer to leave it for now, and return to the idea of polarity in organic life.

While we may argue about the mechanism by which electro-magnetic fields affect cells, there is a much better under-standing about how electromagnetic waves are propagated and subsequently received by, let us say, the aerial in our radio sets, so that we can receive the transmitted radio programme.

Aerials are polar too, or rather bi-polar. That is to say they are made up of two lengths of conductive material just long enough to receive the waves of electromagnetic energy which have been transmitted. By making them specific lengths they can receive specific signals. Take a look at the FM radio aerial on someone's roof and compare it with the TV aerial on your own: the FM aerial has lateral 'sticks' which are longer and further apart than those on the TV aerial. This is simply because the TV transmissions are at frequencies which are higher – and therefore wavelengths which are shorter – than those being sent out by the FM radio transmitter.

In the early days of radio, engineers designed carefully constructed helical radio aerials, because they found them very efficient at collecting signals. Today we use straight aerials because they are simpler to make. It is curious that the DNA in every cell nucleus is also helically twisted, and that it has a negatively-charged and positively-charged end. Of course, the DNA is incredibly small compared with our own aerials, but it is nevertheless capable of receiving signals, and its shorter length can receive frequencies much higher than those used in TV transmission. The *chromosomes* in which the DNA strands are situated are also structures capable of receiving electromagnetic signals, indeed the chromosomes look more like the TV aerials of the 1950s, which were designed like crosses.

Nature, which has been around for many millions of years, may well have discovered all there is to know about radio signal propagation and reception long before humans managed it in this century! The first commercial radio broadcast only went out in 1920, and the first TV broadcasts really only started in the late 1940s (the early 1950s in Great Britain). Before that there had never been any artificially created electromagnetic waves on the planet to speak of.

The length of any aerial gives us a clue to the wavelength it is 'tuned' to receive. Furthermore, there is a fixed relationship between the wavelength of any electromagnetic (EM) radiation and its frequency. This relationship is fixed for all EM energies, from x-rays, to the tiny radiations which emanate from the wiring in your house – or even the radiations which can come from organic cells.

Using this information, we can safely say that if a chromosome is indeed an aerial of some sort, then it is tuned to receive frequencies of around 10^{15} Hz, and if further the DNA was also a receiving aerial, then it would be best fitted to receive frequencies of around 10^{16} Hz.

Amazingly, the brains of all cerebrate creatures do actually give out EM waves, a discovery which was only made in the 1920s by Hans Berger. (Others had already found similar radiations coming from the brains of animals, but it was still such a surprise that Berger kept quiet about the discovery for nearly ten years in case his medical colleagues ridiculed him.) However the brain waves – or alpha and beta rhythms as they are called – are much lower in frequency than those for which DNA and the chromosomes seem to be prepared. Alpha rhythms are only alternating at about 20 cycles per second (or 20 Hertz, to use the correct jargon). The reason for this may be that such frequencies are *carrier waves*: microwave transmissions are often pulsed at extra low frequencies (ELF) so that the signals can penetrate opaque materials like water for instance. Since human beings and other creatures are mostly made of water, it would make sense for a transmitting brain to pulse the coded signals at extra low frequencies.

When you listen to your radio you tune to specific frequencies. By changing the tuning from one frequency to another you can miraculously hear quite different signals – the news on one channel, say, and a symphony on another – even though the frequencies are not very far apart. Of course we have all become used to this now, but only a few decades ago it was still a marvel. The amount of information which can be conveyed by all these different frequencies, provided the receiving aerial and associated amplifier collect the incoming signals properly, is huge. However, very early on it was also realized that if the signals are *too* close together they could 'jam' the broadcast.

No one stopped to think what might happen if the body's own signals were jammed, disturbing its delicate morphology. Or, conversely, that specific signals might help the body repair itself. Yet one of the most important unsolved problems in biology – the miracle which initiates the splitting of one cell into two (*mitosis*) and protein synthesis – might well be explained by this sort of telecommunication.

Biologists divide cellular cycles into four parts. In the first part the cell is at rest (called the G1 phase). Then it suddenly starts to create (or synthesize) protein molecules; this is the S phase (synthesis phase). Again there follows a waiting period, during which nothing much happens (the G2 phase). Then the cell suddenly starts to split into two; this is the M phase (the mitosis phase).

The process of protein synthesis coincides with a period called 'paradoxical sleep', a period when, though the body's activity is totally inert, for some unknown reason the brain's activity reaches its highest level. Because biologists couldn't explain why the brain was so active when the body was so quiescent, they called the phenomenon 'paradoxical'.

Some 85 per cent of protein synthesis takes place during paradoxical sleep. Could it be that the brain, so far away, is responsible for the initiation not only of this process, but also of mitosis itself, and that it instructs protein synthesis by somehow telecommunicating with the individual cells at a distance, completely unconnected by any neural or chemical pathways?

The hypothesis is an exciting one; but how could it do this?

The human brain is divided into two halves, known as the cerebral hemispheres. No one has ever stopped to ask why this is, let alone explain it. Perhaps the facts of electromagnetic polarity can shed some light on the subject.

The two halves of the brain are connected by millions of strands of nervous tissue, each fibre passing from a great pyramidal shaped cell in the *cortex* at one side of the brain to an identical pyramidal cell on the other side. These large cells themselves have *dendrites*, at their tops which associate with the pyramidal cells nearby. They are also polarized, and the cells' polarity can be changed by an organ called the *thalamus*, situated underneath the strands of *commissural fibres* – which, incidentally, are called the *corpus callosum* because they are harder than most intracranial cells and tissues – (see figure 1.1).

This system allows not only a controlled flow of ions to pass along the corpus callosum – controlled in that the thalamus can allow one single flow by changing the polarity of a single pyramidal cell – but it can also cause many thousands of pyramidal cells to change polarity at any one time. In other words it can act like a radio station, with the amazing difference that it can cause millions of transmissions of signal at once if required. It is these transmissions which we crudely register on our electrocephalographic instruments as alpha

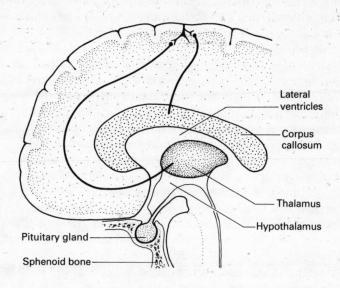

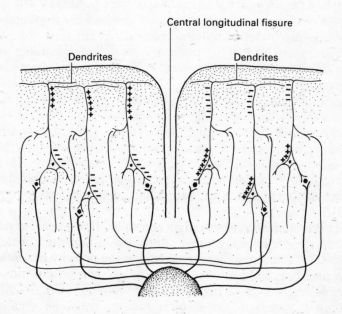

Figure 1.1: The human brain from front to back showing an enlarged view of the cortex.

rhythms, though the specific signals are likely to be much faster in frequency. These myriad complex signals could well be what triggers protein synthesis and mitosis.

A physicist would immediately point out that all electro-magnetic signals get weaker – attenuate – with distance, so how could such weak signals reach as far as, say, the toes or ankles? You can calculate just how strong such signals would have to be to do this, since there are clear rules for the distance any EM signal is likely to travel. In order to perform this calculation, you would need to know the strength of the signal, its frequency and wavelength. Moreover, you would want the transmitter to be as directional as possible, so that transmissions in the wanted direction would be at a greater gain than in the unwanted directions. Finally, if the aerial was an elegant and efficient system it would make sure that the signals only going a short distance would be kept weaker than those going a long way, to conserve energy.

Amazingly, nature seems to have anticipated both problems: even before the beginning of this century, and certainly by the 1950s, physiologists had mapped out the connections between the various parts of the body and their sensory and motor equivalents in the cerebral cortex. A curious discovery emerged: the parts of the body furthest from the brain were by and large controlled from those areas of the cortex nearest together, and vice versa. So if one applies the principles of electromagnetic radiation to the individual pyramidal cells and their connections, the cell pairs connected nearest together on either side of the cortex would emit the strongest signals, while those pairs furthest apart would emit the weakest signals.

It looked as if the brain was designed economically so that the strongest signals from the pyramidal cells were associated with the parts of the body furthest from the brain. A glance at the diagram (figure 1.2), which is redesigned from the original mapping of cerebral motor and sensory areas by Wilder Penfield in the 1950s, will help understand the idea. There are two exceptions – the two major drives of self-preservation (immune defence), and self-procreation (the sex drive) – which are so important that I have devoted a separate chapter to them.

The corpus callosum is also designed to provide the optimum transmissions towards the main part of the body. It is curved slightly towards the body rather than away for it, and

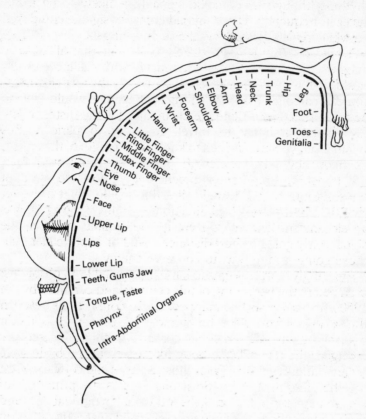

Figure 1.2: Penfield's homunculus

in this way 95 per cent of transmissions radiate towards the body and only 5 per cent radiate away from it upward through the skull. In fact the skull itself acts like a sort of reflector, helping the efficiency of the signal.

Since men have literally thicker skulls than women, these signals, which seem to deteriorate with age, have increasing difficulty in reaching the hair follicles on the male head, which is why men are more prone to baldness than women. But if one examines the pattern of male baldness, sure enough the pattern is that which would occur from attenuation of EM signals from the corpus callosum! The polar diagram of the callosic aerial would have side lobes, and the centre and top of the head would always have the weakest signals. By

increasing signal strength in that direction (or by reamplifying
the existing signal) one would therefore expect that hair on the
head would start to grow again. And this does actually happen
– our first example of electrohealing.

We sleep at night, when the electromagnetic energy of the
sun no longer radiates on our side of the earth, because the
EM environment is less perturbed. And if we start interfering
with the light-dark cycle by switching on electric light in the
winter evenings, this acts as a stressor which can make us
become depressed. We tend to put on weight in the winter
because our brains can spend more time during the longer
nights instructing for protein synthesis. As one ponders the
possibility that this is the underlying mechanism of health,
more facts seem to fit.

The way our brains are structured at last makes sense, after
centuries of incomprehension. For example, the thalamus,
which controls the polarity of the pyramidal cells, is situated
immediately below the corpus callosum. In this way it can
monitor the precise signals being emitted. It can instruct the
hypothalamus to hand over or regain control of motor and
sensory activity which is under the auspices of the pituitary
gland during sleep. Why is the pituitary gland seated deep in
its bunker – the sphenoid bone – if not to carry out as quietly
as possible its role of maintaining life-support systems during
the all-important transmissions?

Cerebral morphogenetic radiation

The concept of cerebral morphogenetic radiation (CMR) is
such a new idea in biology that a good deal of further research
is necessary before we can be sure about it. If it is right, then
we can at last understand the mechanism of morphology – how
the brain can tell the body which cells to repair and when, so
as to preserve its integrity and health.

During the last few centuries a number of medical
practitioners, not to mention some quacks, have tried to tinker
with these mechanisms, with better or worse results. Because
they did not fully understand what they were playing with
however, they were not very successful. Even from earliest
times it was discovered that magnets could have a beneficial
effect on health. The ancients even knew about *geopathic stress*
– and would only build on a plot if sheep were happy to graze

there. Geopathic stress is ill-health which arises from living above areas of sharp geomagnetic anomaly – these can be caused by underground streams or geological faultlines.

The Chinese applied magnets to injured limbs, as well as using the magnetized floating needle to find south. The Greeks evidently knew about it: the very word electricity comes from the Greek word for amber, which if rubbed generates a static electrical charge and hence a spark. It is said they would apply a torpedo fish, which can give a nasty electric shock, to limbs in order to relieve pain. Arab physicians also thought it might be useful as a treatment for gout. In 1667 Athanasius Kircher, though he didn't actually concern himself with its bio-effects, wrote a treatise on it. But the first medical practitioners to evaluate magnetism seriously were Paracelsus and Sir William Gilbert.

In 1600 Gilbert published his monumental *De Magnete*, in which he proclaimed that the earth acted like a bar magnet. His studies were followed up by von Guericke, who invented the first static electrical generating machine. After him Stephen Gray discovered that a human subject could be electrified, and published his observations in the 1731 *Philosophical Transactions* in a paper called 'Experiments concerning electricity'.

Though Faraday recognized the effects of moving magnets in creating an electric field, the 1700s were a watershed of discovery in magnetism too, with a number of experiments applying both forces to human and animal tissues, with the objective of seeing how the body worked or if they could cure ailments thereby. Johan Schaeffer, published a work called *Electrical Medicine* in Regensberg as early as 1752.

In what must be one of the most fortuitous accidental discoveries of all time, one of Luigi Galvani's assistants at the University of Bologna happened quite by accident to touch the nerve to the muscles of a frog leg with his scalpel while a static electrical machine was operating close by. Every time the machine made a spark the muscle contracted – obviously the electrical force had somehow gone through the air to act at a distance on the metal in contact with the nerve. The charge had subsequently gone down the nerve to cause muscular contraction.

By 1793, first Galvani and then Volta had discovered that two dissimilar metals could also induce a steady stream of electricity capable of making a muscle move, and introducing a controversy which was to continue for a century and a half: was there or was there not electricity in living things? Curiously it was left to Humboldt, the geologist, to show that electricity existed both in the flow of currents between dissimilar metals and *per se* in animals.

Galvani was a physician as well as professor of anatomy at Bologna. Yet it was his nephew Giovanni Aldini, a physicist with no medical knowledge, who first tried applying electric currents to schizophrenic patients, reporting a steady improvement in their personality. Another pioneer was Abbe Nollet. He tried unsuccessfully to apply electric currents to those people who were suffering from paralysis.

Interest in electricity and in magnetism swept Europe during the first years of the nineteenth century. It reached as far north as Copenhagen, where Hans Christian Oersted finally uncovered the connection between the two forces in another accidental discovery. In 1820 he happened to be giving a lecture demonstrating voltaic electricity when he noticed that a compass which stood near his machine moved every time he completed the circuit. By July of that year he had published the observation that 'an electrical current flowing in a conducting wire generates a circular magnetic field round the conductor'. Oersted had finally discovered the synthesis of electromagnetism.

Shortly afterwards, using Nobeli's newly invented 'galvanometer', Carlo Matteucci proved beyond a doubt that electrical current was generated from injured tissue, and that serially stacking such tissues could multiply the current in exactly the same fashion as adding more plates to a Voltaic pile. Bioelectromagnetics was truly born.

Thereafter discoveries followed apace: Du Bois Reymond in Berlin made the important discovery of nervous conduction, and the great von Helmholtz measured its speed. Around the same time, and within another discipline, Virchow had found that all disease was the result of cell pathology. Against such a background it was hardly surprising that many should try to heal the body using electrical currents, often without any idea at all of their basic physical mechanisms.

As early as 1843 Eydam had published a thesis on the application of a magnetic field to the human body for therapeutic purposes. In 1878 Charcot and Reynard told of the effects of magnetism on hysteria, and in 1878 Westphal and Gangee reported how abnormal skin sensations were returned to normal on the application of magnetism. In the same year Waldmann published his paper on 'Der Magnetismus in der Heilkunde', probably the first thesis concerning the application of a magnetic field to the treatment of illness.

That such biological effects could be produced was of some concern to the power generation and transmission authorities of the time, just as it is today. F. Peterson and A. E. Kennelly of the Edison research laboratory claimed that magnetism had no effect on the human body. L. Hermann reported finding no changes in frogs and humans (today the poor rat is made to bear the brunt of experimental work) following exposure to magnetism. Edison was also crafty enough to make sure that the first electrocution of a criminal was carried out using his rival Westinghouse's alternating currents, rather than the direct currents which he was developing at the time.

Experimental work continued, though somewhat abated and considered disreputable. By 1884, according to Bigelow, '10,000 physicians within the borders of the United States use electricity as a therapeutic agent daily in their practice.' However, without any scientific base, or the benefit of today's precise instruments, the doctors were working in the dark, and electrotherapy became unsupportable following the Flexner report of 1910. This report, commissioned by the Carnegie Foundation, remodelled medical practice on sound scientific principles. So it was that electrochemistry – whose effects are so much easier to measure – rather than electromagnetics – whose mechanisms are still imperfectly understood today – became the accepted basis for curative treatment.

During the early years of the twentieth century, Albert Abrams in the United States was discovering that human beings reacted to even the most minute electronic currents, and indeed seemed to emit them. Meanwhile European researchers like Kurella, Kuehn, Moll, Payr, and Kahame were presenting the baffling evidence of curious bio-effects; baffling and curious in that no mechanism was available to explain magnetism itself (quantum field theory was scarcely in its infancy) let alone its effects on organic life.

The subsequent discovery of antibiotics heralded the death blow, for the time being, of research into electrotherapy, along with magnetotherapy, its baby cousin. If it hadn't been for the

laziness of Alexander Fleming, and the assiduousness of
Florey, antibiotics might otherwise perhaps have been
ignored, and complementary radiative techniques, such as
haemo-irradiation, already emerging in post First World War
Germany, would by now be curing many of today's
electromagnetic disorders. As it was, pharmaceuticals held
sway and its corporations grew massively in size to the
multinational giants they are today. As we shall see, however,
there are disorders which can never be cured by
pharmaceutical or antibiotic means.

Haemo-irradiation was not the only baby thrown away with
the bio-electromagnetic bathwater. Albert Abrams' diagnostic
and curative techniques based on his 'electronic reactions',
though pursued by Boyd in Scotland with such success that
he baffled a visiting investigative team from the Royal Society
of Medicine, also foundered through his inability to explain
how they might work.

Most of the work done in the 1960s used very strong
magnetic fields: Madeleine Barnothy used several thousand
Oersteds in testing for cellular change. (An Oersted is an old
measure of magnetic field strength.) In 1972 Degen was
experimenting with a constant magnetic field of 450 to 530
Gauss – a thousand times the field strength of the earth –
applying it to the hands of patients suffering from Dupuytren's
contracture, incurable by drugs. In the 1960s Dietrich Beischer
was finding out through work on squirrel monkeys that a
20,000 gauss field did not seem to have any noticeable
beneficial effect, except in the case of toothache; and Sinkareva
reported in 1970 that a constant magnetic field was effective
in treating chronic inflammatory illnesses of the female sexual
organs. Most of these researchers were only vaguely aware that
the electromagnetic environment of our planet was steadily
increasing, and that a variety of disorders was emerging which
were proving resistant to the wonder-drugs resulting from
antibiotic medicine.

Nevertheless, the literature was growing sufficiently for Paul
Speigler in 1962 to have published his *Bibliography of the
Biological Effects of Magnetic Fields*. Other landmark
publications to have appeared were Yuri Kholodov's *Effects of
Electromagnetic and Magnetic Fields on the Central Nervous
System*, Alexander Presman's *Electromagnetic Fields and Life*
(1970), Barnothy's *Biological Effects of Magnetic Fields* in 1964

and 1969, or Nakagawa's conference paper on 'Magnetic fields and living bodies' in 1973.

Even so, it was only in the mid-1970s that serious research into magnetotherapy attempted once more to evaluate and understand the mechanisms of its healing action at a distance.

In 1974 Dwyer reported from Australia on the successful use of electrical stimulation for spinal fusion. The first edition of the *Bioelectromagnetics Society Magazine* appeared in 1979, and the *Journal of Bioelectricity* two years later. Both confined their published papers to peer-reviewed scientific work of the highest respectability. And slowly the world began to take notice: at the 1990 BEMS conference, some 400 delegates attended (compared with 260 the previous year).

If ever there was a new, soundly-based science being reborn, these are the sure signs of its genesis. This time, there will be no argument. In the 1990 issue of the *Journal of Bioelectricity*, Mays Swicord and his co-workers reported confirmation of Reba Goodman's earlier findings that cells exposed to an asymetric 72Hz signal for even as little as six hours showed shifts in the pattern of protein synthesis (thus incidentally supporting a part of my CMR hypothesis). Swicord concluded:

Enough data are available to state the gene expression can be enhanced or inhibited by exposure to weak time-varying magnetic fields. The response is signal and locus specific, i.e. different sets of genes are being affected by exposure to signals of different time characteristics. A well established mechanism is not yet available.

This paper is in effect saying that at the sort of frequencies known to emanate from the human brain (15 cycles per second) specific electromagnetic signals can increase or inhibit the speed with which cells complete part of their cell cycle (synthesis). This paper emerged not from some unheard of minor university, but from the Center for Devices and Radiological Health of the Federal Drug Administration (FDA), one of the most powerful scientific voices in the world.

We have come a long way from that primitive early research. It is time that the work of Dr Abrams whose 'Black Box' – an oscilloclast, i.e. a receiver tuned to specific frequencies to relate to specific human diseases – brought him infamy instead of fame in the first decades of this century, was re-evaluated in

the light of our fresh knowledge. It was Abrams who, in those
non-radio days, put electrohealing into practice for the first
time. After him came the whole school of radionics, whose
modern practitioners are still thought of by many as
disreputable, and whose methods are known to very few.

In the next chapter we take a look at what they have to say,
and at the whole field of non-invasive electromagnetic
diagnosis.

2. New Discoveries in Electro-diagnosis

Everyone, including the medical profession, would readily agree that treating the cause is the best way of coping with any illness.

Julian Kenyon, *Twenty-first Century Medicine* (1986)

Current methods by which health disorders are diagnosed border on the antidiluvian. It never fails to surprise me that the ordinary general practitioner continues to tolerate the existing British system: the crowded waiting rooms filled with people who have had to come there feeling unwell, only to wait perhaps an hour before being seen by the doctor; the invariable pill- or potion-based prescription after a five-minute diagnosis; the rather ugly commercial motive behind the scenes.

Doctors get paid for the number of people on their panel; the drug companies supply pills at the most profitable price possible, against a background of virtually no competition as a result of protectionist practices. The patients feel increasingly that the medical profession is failing them.

After the frantic surgery hours come home-visits, often to chronically unwell patients, spiced with the occasional emergency. No wonder doctors have double the suicide rate of ordinary folk and seem to lose the human touch. No wonder that alternative therapies are gaining ground, too often as a last resort, and are now believed to have been sought by a quarter of all patients, despite being rubbished by the conventional medical press.

The scene within our hospitals is hardly any better: nurses and junior doctors exploited unmercifully to the limit of their physical endurance for the sake of financial expediency; the year-long queues for surgical operations; a dwindling level of national health service; a medical philosophy based on curative rather than preventive medicine. It cannot go on: and it does not have to. This chapter reviews new emerging diagnostic methods which pressage a paradigm-shift in the practice of twenty-first century medicine, based on electronics and electromagnetics rather than on pharmaceuticals and electro-chemistry.

The first difference is that electro-diagnosis does not wait for overt symptoms to appear. The first signs of AIDS, for example are neurological disturbances in the brain long before any observable opportunistic infection sets in. Refinements in EEG technology now make it easy to check brain activity. That each of us has a unique brain pattern is well known to the EEG technician, who, with a little practise can not only distinguish between one person's EEG record from another, but can also recognize when that pattern has changed, registering a pre-disease condition. Computer software has now been developed to do this same comparison job automatically. And since EEG data is eminently suitable for capture on electromagnetic tape, it should be a short step from there to the development of personal EEG analysers.

If the doctor's surgery still exists in the next century, its attendees would be able to use their waiting-time getting a brain scan ready for the physician from apparatus in the surgery installed there for the purpose, instead of thumbing aimlessly through last year's magazines. The advent of cheap electronics also means that some patients may even be able to keep a personal scanner at home for regular check-ups.

Isobel Maxwell Cade has been developing her late husband's 'Mind Machine' to show the curious patterns of excitation which the brain emits. The flashing lights on its console are meaningless to the lay observer, but she has grown capable of interpreting these signals to indicate the emotional state of her subjects. Edward Bach needed no more than this information to administer highly effective flower remedies for the kinds of ailments which fill our surgeries today.

In the 1950s, Reinholdt Voll, a German doctor, was among the first to realize that the electromagnetic emissions from the body and brain offered the possibility of diagnosis. At the beginning of the century Abrams had already recognized that the electromagnetic characteristics of any person changed with disease, just as Professor Golla at the Maudsley had surmised the same in respect of brain rhythms in the 1930s. Voll extended this to the acupuncture points and found that electrical resistance was considerably different when patients were ill from when they were healthy. The acupuncture point is electrically negative with respect to its surrounding skin.

Voll found this effect was not only subcutaneous but also on the surface of the skin, and built a complicated system of disease diagnosis based on that discovery, using an apparatus which he called the Vegatest machine. He found that in disease the voltage indicator fell, but could be equilibriated by certain substances which, when placed in the circuit which included the patient, acted as a balancing resistance.

In the modern Vegatest machine the homoeopathic approach differs from classical homoeopathy in that several different substances (rather than only one) may be introduced simultaneously into the circuitry in order to obtain equilibrium. Having found out which remedies eliminated falls in the indicator, Voll then simply applied these to the patient, and claimed to achieve good results. Though his concepts and the Vegatest machine were rapidly adopted in Germany, it did not find much favour elsewhere, because the diagnostics were very complex, and relied heavily on the skill of the operator.

Voll's ideas were further extended by Dr Helmut Schimmel. Schimmel used just one point on the patient and took as the diagnostic indicator sealed ampoules containing homoeopathic extracts from various normal mammalian organs, such as the liver. The patient is still wired into the low-voltage circuit. However, both the Voll and Vegatest approaches still depend on a high level of operator skill to find which substances will balance the circuit, and also rely on a definite subjective judgement. Moreover, diagnosis and treatment can be affected by minute variations in the geomagnetic field (geopathic stress), by powerlines and other man-made components of our daily electromagnetic environment. And the absence of a proven biological mechanism makes interpretation of the results difficult.

A slightly different approach, leading to a whole class of diagnostic machines, is where an electromagnetic input signal of some sort is fed into the patient and the emerging variations on this are interpreted in terms of morbidity. An early example of this is the Segmental electrogram, also developed by Dr Schimmel, which does not provide the finer details available from Vegatest machines. Whereas the Vegatest applies a tiny current, the SEG applies a 13-Hz 2-volt current via four pairs of 6 cm electrodes placed at either side of the head, thorax, abdomen, and pelvis respectively. The current is first passed negatively, then reversed. The resulting potential differences are recorded on a chart (or into a computer) and diagnosis consists of seeing just how large a change in potential exists between the eight electrodes, so that each quadrant of the body can be measured.

Where the differential is very small some dysfunction is to be expected. The SEG gives a crude indication, but cannot identify precisely which specific organ or tissues are faulty. It probably obtains its effect from the disturbance to its circuit from injury currents of the kind noted by Becker, but cannot indicate precisely where the injury currents are arising.

More recently, Dr William Nelson, a computer expert and electrical engineer from Las Vegas, has designed his 'Eclosion System EPFX Biofeedback System' to diagnose illness. This is basically a series of sensors measuring resistance, impedance, voltage, amperage, resonant frequencies, oscillations, temperature, and other parameters of the body. The results are fed back to the same body. (The word eclosion derives from the biological term for a butterfly emerging from its cocoon).

Surprisingly the system has gained FDA approval – based on its function as a thermometer – but in fact it presents a much deeper picture of the body than was available before. Conceptually the patient's 'life force' is measured in amperage or current. Should this start to fail or wane then the patient's health is deteriorating. Voltage, (the pressure behind that amperage) is controlled by the catecholamines which comprise our different adrenal hormones. So this variant of the biofeedback machines is translating endocrine function into electrical terms.

A computer linked to the Eclosion machine also collects data on blood scores, urine, blood tests, and other physical parameters over a 15-minute logging span to gain a complex picture of the total health components of the patient. Similar machines have been designed in Russia. Professor Gulayev recently revealed details of his machine in the United Kingdom which is available for export from Russia.

From Golden, Colorado, Computer Applied Technology make another electro-diagnostic machine, the Molecular Emission Scanner, first designed in 1985. It was developed originally during the mid-1970s by Hank Blair and Bob Dratch, based on a supersensitive spectral analyser.

This scanner does not actually touch the patient's body, its sensor is held some three inches away from the skin. First a baseline is set by pointing it at a neutral energy spot such as over the sacrum. A chart recorder prints out the 'before treatment' conditions. After this the relevant therapy, homoeopathic or otherwise, is performed, then the area is re-scanned to see if the readings all conform to the normal conditions as already registered.

The device is said to be hypersensitive, so precautions have to be taken to prevent interference from outside sources, even as far as constructing a Faraday shield if necessary. (A Faraday shield or cage is a box made of soft iron – often mu-metal, an iron alloy – which shields from external electric (non magnetic) fields.) Signatures from subjects are printed out as hard copy showing the fluctuations above and below the reference point, and an examination of these is said to indicate the pathology of the subject. Again the scanner is probably picking up the injury currents emanating from the body, with different signatures depending on the injury.

Not all electro-diagnostic instruments are as unconventional or controversial as those above. Nor are they used only by alternative medical practitioners. Perhaps the most obvious electro-diagnostic devices, apart from the EEG itself, are the nuclear magnetic resonance imaging (MRI) and computerized axial tomographic (CAT) scanning machines. These do not claim to indicate specific malfunctions, but are simply providing detailed images of interior organs such as the brain. The CAT scanner was invented in the beginning of the 1970s, and is now used widely throughout the world. In the United Kingdom GEC's Picker subsidiary and EMI have been the principal manufacturers. The idea of the CAT scanner is that it fires thin x-ray beams through the brain while revolving around it. The x-rays activate crystals on the other side of the scanned organ and the attenuation of the signal thus received is computed and amalgamated with thousands of readings so as to build up a 3 dimensional picture of the interior. Conventional x-rays can only show a two dimensional result from the various opaque substances through which the x-rays traverse.

Since simple rotation will not by itself distinguish between opacity caused by one high-density spot and opacity caused by a radial of even low density, a number of one dimensional projections of the slice must be measured at different parts of the rotation, and from these an image can be obtained. To obtain a detailed two-dimensional picture each point has to be scanned many times, and so a very large number of readings are taken.

Even so, the CAT scanner is 100 times more sensitive than the conventional x-ray system, to such an extent that variations in soft tissues of nearly similar density can be displayed. As a diagnostic tool the CAT scan is simply a sophisticated photograph, and though it will identify tumours within the brain, their cause or aetiology is not thereby explained. Early identification of tumours may make post-phylactic surgery possible, however, and the benefits of the CAT scanner have been recognized as a major contribution to medical diagnostic imaging. The long-term effects of low-level x-radiation of the brain are, however, still uncertain.

Another perhaps less hazardous method of electromagnetic diagnosis is nuclear magnetic resonance imaging. In this technique a strong static magnetic field is applied to the organism, which causes all its atoms to line up in the field. Then a brief RF signal is emitted and the time taken by the atoms to realign provides information on the density of the internal structures of the organism.

The possibility that organic life can actually emit its own radiations, and that these change with illness, has encouraged researches directed towards the strange phenomenon of Kirlian photography. The Kirlian story only began in this century. It is well described by Peter Tompkins and Christopher Bird in their superlative bestseller *The Secret Life of Plants:*

In a small apartment in Krasnovar, Russia, a corner of which was fitted out as a miniature laboratory, Semyon Davidovich Kirlian, an electrician and amateur photographer, and his wife, Valantina, were making some adjustments to equipment they had begun building two years before the Nazi attack on their country.

With their new invention they had discovered they could

photographically reproduce, without lens or camera, a strange luminescence which seemed to issue from all living things but was unapprehensible from the human eye.

A knock on the door surprised them, as no visitor was likely to call at that time of the evening; they were even more surprised when a total stranger announced he had come all the way from Moscow to see if they could make for him photographs of the strange energy which he had heard they alone could make visible on film. From his briefcase the stranger pulled two identical leaves and handed them to the Kirlians.

Excited at the prospect that their discovery was to be put to an official test, the Kirlians stayed up until after midnight, but were disappointed to note that while they could make excellent pictures of energy flares from one of the leaves, they could get only a weak facsimile from the other. They worked on through the night, trying to get photos of the luminescence as similar as the leaves themselves, but were wholly unsuccessful.

In the morning, crestfallen, they showed their results to the scientist, who shouted in amazement: 'But you've found it! You've proved it photographically!' He explained that one leaf had been plucked from a healthy plant, the other from a diseased specimen. Although the two leaves appeared identical to the human eye, the pictures plainly differentiated between them. Illness was evidently manifest in a plant's energy field before becoming visible as a symptom in its physical body.

The Kirlian photograph of a leaf part of which has been cut off and removed will still show the whole leaf. This is known as the 'phantom leaf effect'. Moreover, the colours of a Kirlian photograph show the physiological action of the sweat glands in the skin, hence the emotional state of the subject. People claiming to see the aura also often claim that its colour changes according to the emotional state of the subject. Finally Kirlian photos vary with pH value of the skin. This pH factor is dealt with elsewhere in the book, but it is significant that cancer patients show virtually no Kirlian corona discharge, having a low pH factor on their skin's surface.

From his interest in Kirlian photography, one researcher has developed equipment to detect imbalances in human beings as a result of illness. More than that, he claims to be able to correct these imbalances by application of the correct frequencies. His latest range of hand-held machines seems similar to those featured in science fiction movies and his personally trained pupils use them around the world.

In my book *The Dark Side of the Brain*, I described Kirlian photography, and its contribution to the early diagnosis of disease, in some depth.

In Romania during the 1970s, Dr Ion Dumitrescu was pursuing an equally novel method of electrographic imaging, also inspired by the original work of the Kirlians. Thanks to Julian Kenyon, an enlightened British doctor who practises energetic medical techniques at his Southampton clinic, Dumitrescu's work was translated into English in the early 1980s.

Kenyon had become dissatisfied with Kirlian photography because he found that its images were not easily reproducible. He also felt that many of the features seen in a Kirlian image were due to an artefact, in other words that they were not caused by the organism, but by the currents from the equipment itself. (Others who claimed to diagnose disease from Kirlian handprints were also often using subjective unreplicable opinions which brought the technique into disrepute.)

Dumitrescu pioneered the mapping of the minute electromagnetic changes which continually occur in organic tissues. Using high voltages, he thought, was too crude and overpowering a diagnostic method. Accordingly he confined his techniques to low voltages and used a single impulse, thus pioneering electronography rather than electroluminescence, so that there was minimum secondary interference with the fields emanating from the investigated organism. In a way it was like x-radiation photography, but at non-ionizing frequencies.

Since 1962 Dumitrescu has used his technique of electronography to expose acupuncture points (called by Kenyon electrodermal points) on the body. These are found to exhibit increased electrical conductivity, higher electrical potential than the surrounding skin, and increased electrical capacitance. The points appeared, moreover, to be connected functionally to particular organs or tissues, and were subject to electrical activation in pathological conditions.

Thus the points could be used as diagnostic indicators, since they only appeared when there was a dysfunction or diseased state. By comparing the electronographs of nearly 900 patients,

Dumitrescu was able to diagnose diseases simply by means of the electronographically exposed acupuncture points, even though the points did not always appear at the sites of traditional acupuncture locations.

Each image revealed a dark central zone of irregular shape and with a diameter of 1-2 cm, surrounded by a luminous centre. Becker had found similar gradients of electrical potential round acupuncture points too. In acute diseases the epidermal points, as Dumitrescu called them, were larger and more numerous, which seemed to be a startling confirmation of the body's electrical equivalent of its disease. The eruptions of marginal discharges were due to a current of ionized air, polarized around the central point, very much as Becker found. It seems that these points are entry or exit points for air-ions.

Dumitrescu also explored the use of electronography in cancer research, and investigated some 171 malignant tumours. He found that the image was different in some two thirds of the cases, and that in some cases electronography identified tumours not found by x-ray photography.

Summarizing his conclusions, Dumitrescu clearly identifies malignancy with a reduction in neg-ions:

The disappearance or reduction in the layer of detectable adherent aeroions is a phenomenon which can be explained through the perturbations secondary to those produced by the tumour on the biological electrical medium. These perturbations translate either into diminution of ionization capacity of air in the vicinity of the body, or into diminution of attraction exercised by the organism on the structured aeroions, or through a combination of both phenomena. Therefore the question of malignant tumours acting as a radiation source becomes a possibility.

This behaviour suggests the possibility of the existence of biological radiation in the ultraviolet region which is more intense in areas of neoplasia. These observations allow us to revert to the hypothesis made by Gurwitsch some 40 years ago, when he demonstrated the influence of malignant experimental tumours on the growth of vegetable tissues. Recent research carried out in the USA and the USSR has lent support to Gurwitsch's observations.

(Aeroions are particles which are electrically charged by having gained or lost an electron. Since electrons are negatively charged, aeroions which have lost an electron are positively-charged and vice-versa. Electrons can quite easily get knocked off their associated atoms.)

If pathological changes can be detected at the stage of electrical charges in the body before the appearance of tumour, then we are on the eve of a very early diagnosis of malignancy – a benefit crucial to the management of such disorders.

3. Magnets and Health: The Hope of a Science?

> Living systems can be affected by many agents in many different ways, but these influences add up to modifications of one basic parameter, the density of electric polarization.

Emilio del Giudice, Physicist, University of Milan, 1990.

Not many people – even fewer scientists – would profess to understand what magnetism really is, and fewer still can explain if or how it affects human cells. The 'hard' scientific peer-reviewed research on magnetic bio-effects is scanty, its results often inconclusive, contradictory or bewildering, and its mechanisms unknown or at best guessed at. By frightening contrast the numbers of bio-magnetic devices claimed to improve the health, or repair the body's disorders, are many, often bolstered by pseudoscientific 'evidence' or by uncontrolled case histories chosen to convince the potential buyer of the profferred apparatus. Can we find any bedrock of fact anywhere, to serve as a starting point?

One starting point must be the way an electron spins, and how the direction of that spin induces a magnetic field near it. Normally, electrons in most atoms orbit their associated nuclei in pairs, with each electron in the pair spinning in opposite directions, so as to balance the other's directional force or 'moment'. Some atoms, however, have single electrons among those orbiting their nucleus, and these clearly cannot be balanced in equilibrium, so they exhibit a directional moment. If the atom (or molecule or ion) includes several such unpaired electrons, which for some reason do not relapse into balanced pairs, then it can produce a strong net directional moment. This force is magnetism: the net directional moment of unpaired electrons. There is no new kind of force needed to explain it other than what we already believe happens inside atoms.

It was called magnetism because a certain kind of stone was discovered to attract iron by an ancient Greek shepherd called Magnes. The atoms in lodestone, made of ferrous oxide, (Fe_3O_4), contain several unpaired electrons.

How does this 'unbalanced' collection of electrons cause other materials, such as an iron pin to be attracted towards it? It is because the two separate materials (magnet and pin) are trying to achieve the equilibrium together which the single material cannot. The reason why opposite electromagnetic charges attract is because of their basic need to reach this equilibrium. As long as the electron spin is not disturbed, its magnetism will endure unchanged. But if thermal agitation (heat) disrupts the spinning electrons by making them change direction, the magnetism declines.

After a certain amount of heating (at a point known as the Curie point) the thermal agitation is greater than the force of the electron spin, and so the material ceases to be magnetic. Another way of disrupting electron spin is to hit the material with a hammer. The physiotherapist does something similar to your muscles when massaging them, which has a relaxing effect as the ions are literally bashed out of you. Both methods can demagnetize any iron bar magnet, as any schoolchild knows. A third way is by 'degaussing', applying a reverse magnetic field to neutralize the spinning electrons.

Although all organic substances are in fact magnetic, or potentially magnetic, in that they are repelled or attracted by a magnetic field – even paper by a rubbed comb – their magnetism is weak (it is called diamagnetism) and depends on the existence of an external field to unbalance the electrons which are normally almost all in pairs. Some materials whose electrons are firmly and happily paired have no net magnetic moment, since their spinning electrons are orbiting the nucleus too far apart to affect each other.

In other materials the spinning electrons line up throughout the material in alternate directions, so that they cancel each other's effect (these are called antiferromagnets); obviously these too are only very weakly magnetic.

However, if and when all the unpaired electrons are spinning in the same direction, the net magnetic moment can be very strong (these are ferromagnets). Being a ferromagnet does not necessarily mean that the substance is made of iron: the chromium dioxide which coats our favourite audio tapes is a ferromagnet.

Turning now to the cell's organic nucleus, and to the DNA within it, we also, of course, find spinning electrons. Of these, by far the most important are the electrons which orbit the hydrogen atoms which alone link the bases on either side of the helices (composed of sugar-phosphate strands).

Hydrogen has only one electron, so by itself is inevitably possessed of a net magnetic moment, and thus unstable. Hydrogen can solve its instability by sharing its single electron with another hydrogen atom, thus achieving equilibrium, and a co-valent bond forms between them. It is a very uneasy partnership however, and it takes very little to persuade the electrons in a co-valent hydrogen bond to go elsewhere.

Not surprisingly therefore, the bonds holding DNA together are incredibly sensitive to magnetic fields generated by any stray unpaired electrons (or ions) which happen to be nearby. Such ions of course are the underlying cause of all electromagnetic fields, and it is their movement *en masse* which gives the moving fields their characteristics of frequency and wavelength.

Now we can see how magnetic fields might affect DNA, by making it easy for the strands to separate. (It is also possible that magnetic fields might help them to stay attached.) The effect of a magnetic field might therefore be to encourage the synthesis of DNA by splitting the strands apart at the right time, as the process of mitosis proceeds. But remember that the DNA strand itself is also polarized along its length, with a positive charge at one end and a negative one at the other. In between there is presumably a gradient of charge. A very specific magnetic field might therefore encourage only a small part of the helix to split, at a very specific point in the strand.

One thing which puzzles cell biologists is that the DNA seems to split not only from one end then gradually unfold, but to do so simultaneously throughout its length. Reba Goodman works in the pathology department of Colombia University. For some years she has been exposing the salivary gland cells from a fly *Sciara coprophila* to a time-varying extra-low-frequency magnetic field, to see if such fields have any biological effect. She has constantly found a higher level of transcription in the exposed cells, whether the field was time or amplitude dependent; also, some of the proteins subsequently produced were not present in the unexposed controls.

Mays Swicord and his co-workers also found not only that such fields affected gene expression – that is the way genes are produced and what sort – but also that different sets of genes were affected by signals of different time characteristics. From such studies it certainly looks as if alternating current (AC) magnetic fields can cause biological effects likely to speed up protein synthesis. In addition, it suggests that unusual proteins can also be synthesized by them, which presumably includes neoplastic or cancerous tissues.

What about static magnetic fields? These are magnetic fields which are not changing their electron spin at all, but which nevertheless have a net magnetic moment. Though his namesake Kyoichi Nakagawa has researched static magnetic treatment at the Isuzu Hospital in Tokyo since the mid-1950s, it was Masayoshi Nakagawa and Yuzo Matsuda, from Japan's Railway Labour Science Research Institute, who reported in 1988 that chronic exposure to a strong (0.6 Tesla) static magnetic field caused rats to avoid shocks less than their unexposed counterparts; in other words, the fields may have been affecting the rats' sensitivity. More than twenty years before that, Madeleine Barnothy had pointed to a possible effect of the magnetic field on the genetic code, but she too had been using very high (0.94 Tesla) magnetic fields. During the 1940s, K. M. Hansen had found that applying magnets to people affected their autonomic nervous system.

Kyoshi Nakagawa suggests that the human body has evolved in the influence of the earth's magnetic field, but that modern living has decreased its effect. He believes that by applying an artificial magnetic field the illnesses which result from this 'magnetic field deficiency syndrome' can be alleviated. He identifies the symptoms of the syndrome as: stiffness of the shoulders, back and scruff of the neck, uncertain lumbago, chest pains for no specific reason, habitual headache, dizziness and insomnia for no apparent reason, habitual constipation, and general lassitude.

An unbalanced autonomic nervous system might also be the

result of magnetic field deficiency. In a 1976 issue of the *Japanese Medical Journal*, Nakagawa reported his original results of tests conducted to relieve stiffness of the shoulders. The patients were asked to wear ferrite permanent magnetic bands in the form of bracelets. This proved highly successful, and another researcher, Fujimoto confirmed the effects in a separate series of tests. Other Japanese scientists Nambu and Kimura issued 1,163 magnetic bracelets and compared their effects with 644 non-magnetized bracelets worn to treat stiffness of the shoulders. Considerable differences were reported between the two groups.

In another series of tests, Nakagawa placed ferrite permanent magnets in the mattresses of hospital patients, and reported subjective improvements, but no clinical differences. In 1974, in one of the largest research projects ever undertaken in this field, Nakagawa distributed questionnaires along with 'patch on the skin' magneto-therapeutic devices, to four groups, totalling 11,648 cases. No ill-effects were reported from use, but the devices were found to be over 90 per cent effective in alleviating muscle pain, with a confidence co-efficient of 99 per cent. A similar level of success was found when necklaces made of rare earth cobalt magnets with a surface flux density of 1300 Gauss were worn.

Another researcher, Horie, in 1976 used magnetic finger rings to test their effects. Again he found that they were 76 to 93 per cent effective in treating shoulder stiffness. Even when the tests were 'blind' there was still a considerable difference between the controls and the cases, so the placebo effect was evidently not responsible for the difference. In general, tests seem to show that the stronger (1300 Gauss) necklaces are more effective than the weaker (200 Gauss) versions.

Our normal electromagnetic environment is not likely to include fields much higher than about 50,000 nanoTesla (the geomagnetic field of the earth) and a typical magnetic field in a house from domestic wiring might only be as high as 2000 nT (2 milliTesla), or some combination of the two.

True, some scientists have pointed out that the earth's geomagnetic field is gradually weakening (at about 0.05 per cent a year), and Charles Brooker and others have been questioned whether the geomagnetic field is stationary, both of which, if true, may make its effect more powerful. But why and how could the tiny magnets used by magneto-therapists affect us so profoundly? The answer could well have been hinted at by none other than Michael Faraday himself.

Faraday had found out that if a static magnet was moved it could induce an electric field, whereas if it was stationary it could not. Only the actual movement caused the induction. Consider a small magnet applied to the skin immediately above a vein or artery, where the blood flows past it underneath the skin. Red blood cells containing haemoglobin – a molecule with four atoms of iron at its centre – must move past the magnet. Inevitably, a small electric current is induced in the iron atoms and then carried around the body, into its finest recesses, including the brain, the lungs and the heart.

The strength of this effect will be influenced by such factors as the north/south alignment of the magnet relative to the blood's flow, the orientation of the person in the earth's magnetic field, and any other electric appliances which might be operating nearby. But how might these induced electric or magnetic fields help or hinder the body as it struggles to maintain its morphology by cell division?

The structure of haemoglobin itself gives us a clue. The iron atom at its centre plays an important role in carrying oxygen round the bloodstream from the lungs to the brain and then the muscles. This iron (Fe) atom (inside the haem), with its unpaired electrons, can pick up and let go oxygen atoms very easily. But it is protected by globulin, which are effectively four pairs of polarized polymer strands, encompassing the haem in such a way that their negative ends and positive ends face each other like four pairs of horseshoes.

This protective arrangement ensures that under normal conditions the haem would not itself become magnetized, or if already magnetized it would not change its magnetic condition. Remember I said that all eukaryotic cells have a nucleus containing DNA? Well, a red blood cell is the exception: it has no nucleus, and no DNA. When one thinks about it, that makes sense: a nearby iron atom whose net magnetic moment is being changed continually as it collects and drops oxygen would be confusing to any DNA functioning as an aerial receiver: the haemoglobin would 'jam' the DNA's reception.

When they do become magnetized, the erythrocytes tend to stack like coins (they are flat discs) as their magnetic fields attract each other, positive to negative. Consider now what might happen if a stray artificial field happens to generate a net magnetic moment in an otherwise stable haemoglobin molecule. It would have a disturbing effect on any other nucleated cells nearby, impairing their reception of incoming signals for DNA synthesis, protein synthesis or for any other reason, such as instructing for morphogenetic integrity.

Another type of blood cell is the T-lymphocyte. These cells confirm which are the cells belonging to the body and which are foreigners. They mark the latter by attaching flags to them for subsequent destruction by the macrophages (which literally gobble them up) or for other kinds of immune system cells to deal with. Unlike tissue cells, T-cells need to circulate freely, and to do this they polarize themselves into magnets, using calcium. In this way they can move towards any magnetic attractive field. Such fields include the currents around an open wound, demyelinated nerve fibres in multiple sclerosis and the piezoelectric currents where bones press together between joints, as in arthritis. T-cells seem to congregate wherever there are unusual electromagnetic fields in the body.

Could it be that magnetized haemoglobin inhibits the circulation of T-lymphocytes, preventing them from fulfilling their cytotoxic (cell-killing) role?

There is some evidence that this is so. In 1988, under the general direction of Ross Adey, researcher Dan Lyle and his colleagues tried to see what would happen if they exposed human T-lymphocytes to very weak EM energy. Would the exposed cells respond just as easily to mark any foreign invaders (called mitogens, because lymphocytes react to them by increasing in numbers, using mitosis to do so)? In fact, exposing T-cells to a mitogen is a good way of seeing whether the T-cells are acting normally, and some well established mitogens, like pokeweed, are often used in this kind of laboratory work.

Sure enough, Lyle found that the cytotoxicity of the exposed T-cells was inhibited by up to 40 per cent compared with unexposed lymphocytes. Further experiments confirmed that it did not matter whether the frequency was ELF or microwave: the lymphocytes were obviously less capable of carrying out their marker function, since they did not proliferate anything like as quickly or as much. In fact, an Italian team (Pio Conti and colleagues) had found the same thing in 1983, and other researchers replicated the findings afterwards (Emilia *et al.* in 1985). There was no doubt about the matter: electromagnetic energy inhibits the vital lymphocyte function of distinguishing between our own cells and those of foreign invaders. The enormous implications of this were rightly treated with some caution by the scientists: to them, how the inhibition occurred was still a mystery.

Unlike the early research into magnetic field bio-effects, the strength of the field sufficient to upset T-cell proliferation was only about the same levels which might be found in our everyday environment. During a decade of research, Ruggero Cadossi at Modena University's Instituto Clinica Medica II used a frequency of 75 Hertz, a pulse width of 1.3 milliseconds, and a field strength of 2 to 3 milliTesla to cause an increase in cell division and a corresponding growth in DNA synthesis. These EM field characteristics are to be found in some homes, though only when the ground return currents are unbalanced. (Such imbalances might be found, for example, where the cabling from electric substations curls round a house rather than enters the transformer in a straight line.)

To return to our journey through the magnetic minefields, and haemoglobin. In trying to understand if and why small magnets applied over the veins or arteries might heal us, remember that haemoglobin is like a magnet with its keepers in place. It could be that the small magnets are degaussing the iron within the haemoglobin, and thus allowing the lymphocytes to improve their functions in identifying invading pathogens. In consequence the pathogens are removed by other parts of the immune system and the infection or disorder goes away. If the distant action of magnetism (and also magnetized haemoglobin) can impair the immune system, then perhaps heating the blood will also have a beneficial effect, by decreasing the net magnetic moment in its haemoglobin. In 1990 it was reported that an AIDS patient had been 'cured' by simply extracting his blood, heating it to 108 degrees Fahrenheit, and then replacing it. The operation was long, difficult, and dangerous, but it seems to have worked: within a few days all the patient's symptoms of AIDS had gone. (I will deal with the whole question of AIDS in a separate book, but this clue suggests we are on the right track.)

When we get ill from a serious infection we often get a fever. The fever seems to be a crucial part of ridding ourselves of the infection: if it is not intense enough the malady is not cured, often with dire consequences. Thucydides remarked in his history of the great plague of Athens that those who suffered the highest fevers were most likely to survive, but his keen observations have gone unnoticed for millennia for lack of anyone wondering why that was, and doctors have been unable to explain why the body often responds in this way when attacked by infection.

I mentioned earlier that haemo-irradiation – a practice gaining favour in the 1940s – had been eclipsed when antibiotics appeared. I did not mention that the radiation was not ionizing (like x-ray therapy) but at ultraviolet frequencies, i.e. frequencies not much faster than visible light. Ultraviolet light is used in butchers' or fishmongers' shops to kill flies, (and also for treating psoriasis, of which more later). In haemo-irradiation, UV light is applied to the patient's blood, and was found to cure atypical pneumonias, herpes, and other symptoms associated with immune deficit.

Its practitioners soon found that it was only necessary to irradiate a small percentage of the blood to effect the cure. Today this form of electro-healing is being revived in Germany, where it started, to treat disorders for which antibiotics and pharmaceuticals have no answer. Applying magnetic fields might also one day be a way of treating Alzheimer's disease. In one curious incident an Alzheimer's patient completely regained his lucidity a few hours after an MRI (magnetic resonance imaging) scan, in which powerful electromagnets are applied to the brain so as to cause the molecules in its cells to orient in the magnetic field. When the magnets are turned off the instrument can obtain an image of the brain and any abnormalities by noting the speed with which the cells return to their original spin positions.

The primary discovery that the two poles of a magnet act to change and alter biological systems was arguably made in 1936, when Dr Roy Davis, quite by accident, noticed that magnets seemed to be affecting the behaviour of two cardboard boxes of earth worms. The event is described in *Magnetism and its Effect on the Living System* (Exposition Press, Florida):

The accidental discovery was made in a small home laboratory built upon leaving grade school and prior to attending the

University of Florida. A large horseshoe magnet was on a wooden work bench near work on a small electronic oscillator used in the old superheterodyne radio circuits in early days of radio. The afternoon had been planned for fishing, and three cardboard containers of earthworms were on the workbench. The earthworms in the cardboard containers were in adequate amounts of black rich soil, with sufficient moisture, and air holes had been punched in the containers.

The covers of the containers were securely fastened to prevent escape. In the process of moving equipment on the work bench the containers of worms were placed unintentionally with one container resting against each end or pole of the magnet, and the other was a distance from the magnet.

As the day progressed additional laboratory work cancelled the fishing plans. The earthworms and containers near the magnet were left in their positions for the rest of that day and night until the following morning. The next morning there was an unexpected experience. The worms had eaten through one side of the container that was resting against the south pole of the horseshoe magnet, while the other containers were in no way changed.

The procedure was repeated, and again over a three-day period the worms ate their way out of the container near the south pole of the magnet. Further refinements established that the 'south pole' worms were fatter and more active, while the 'north pole' worms were thin and slow. Moreover, the waste matter discharged from the exposed worms contained more oils and fats than the controls. The strength of the first magnet was 3000 Gauss. It was found that the lowest strength to cause any effect was about 200 Gauss, and above 4500 Gauss the effects diminished.

Other researchers, like Boe and Salunkhe of Utah State University, confirmed that tomatoes grown near a south pole of a magnet or near an open-ended horseshoe magnet ripened four to six times more quickly than those not near any magnetic fields. Seeds exposed to south field influence also seemed to germinate more quickly and give higher yields at maturity, with the reverse effect from north field influence.

Further research seems to show that small animals, snakes and young chickens are also affected. In one experiment, eight fertile eggs were exposed to a south pole magnetic field of 2500

Gauss and a similar number to north pole energy, while a third group were kept away from any field influence at all. A separate magnet was used for each egg, and the eggs, kept at 80 °F, were turned every three hours. Incubation time proved to be two or three days faster with the S-pole eggs, whereas the N-pole eggs took one or two days longer. After hatching, each of the chicks seemed to spend about two minutes in turns one after another resting between the poles of the real magnet. They would then retire far from it while ignoring a dummy magnet painted to look just like the real one. The experiment was replicated many times, always with the same result. The control chicks also rested between the poles, but for longer (2.5 to 3.5 minutes) and they waited until they were dry after hatching, unlike the S-pole chicks, before exposing themselves to the magnet's field.

Subsequently the S-pole chicks grew faster and stronger than the others, but seemed less intelligent and more cannibalistic, though it is not stated what tests of this finding were made. The N-pole chicks were lighter eaters and in many ways more sensitive to their surroundings than the others, say the researchers. Finally, the N-pole chicks were less sexually active than the controls, while the S-pole chicks were much more active. Unfortunately, one corollary of this was to shorten their lives, and make them more aggressive towards sex partners.

Early researchers into electricity and magnetism, and the inspiration of Galvani, Volta and later Marconi, have given the Italians a continuing scientific interest in electro-magnetic bio-effects. Today at Milan University's physics department, Emilio del Guidice is making his life's work the study of the interaction of magnetism and life. He, like other physicists, applies quantum field theory to these interactions, to explain how ordered biological systems can emerge from non-ordered sets of microscopic components.

Many of us would be surprised to see just how beautifully symmetrical a virus appears under the electron microscope – as if it were a non-living crystal or metallic lattice of iron atoms elegantly arranged together. At this microscopic level there appears to the physicist and biologist alike to be little difference between the living organism and the non-living material.

The gist of del Guidice's hypothesis is this:

Theoretical physics has had a harder life with living systems
(where there are many types of microscopic components, and
hundreds of molecular species in one cell) than with the much
simpler systems investigated in solid-state physics . . . Living
systems can be affected by many agents in many ways but these
influences add up to modifications of this basic parameter, the
density of electric polarization.

What del Guidice appears to be saying is that the very
structures of organic life depend vitally on external EM fields
neither too powerful – otherwise they depolymerize or break
up into their component molecular units – nor too low – or
they are no longer held together by the field's influence. This
in turn implies two things: (a) organic multistructures exist in
a pre-radiated field, and (b) externally influencing those fields
will cause changes, even denaturing, in the multi-structures.
Many decades before, Georges Lakhovsky had said the same
thing: 'Life and disease are simply a war of radiations.'
	Neither Lakhovsky nor del Guidice have pointed out that
cerebral radiations could be responsible for morphology, and
the pre-radiated field. Del Guidice does, however, recognize
the two aspects of EM influence on the filamentary DNA:

Since the EM field is a massive field and not purely transverse,
[radiation pressure] has a longitudinal and a transverse
component. The latter adds up to the gradient force, contributing
to the overall stability of the filament; the former pushes
molecules and ions along the filament in the wave direction.
	It is interesting to note that cytoplasm filaments have been
recognized either at the place where most biochemical reactions
occur, or as the main transport rail system of the cell.

Del Giudice's paper ends by pointing out that the filaments
would themselves emit low intensity coherent electromagnetic
radiation. The empirical confirmation that living cells do emit
ultraweak radiation was reported in 1986 by Fritz Albert Popp,
who took careful measurements of biophoton emissions from
cucumber seeds.
	Del Guidice concludes:

The assimilation of a multicellular biological system to an array of Josephson junctions (these are two semiconductors separated by a barrier) implies that external EM fields, although very weak, could affect in a significant way the normal assets of the system. Experiments on Josephson devices usually require laboratories carefully screened against unwanted electromagnetic perturbations.

The often inconclusive results of cellular studies may indeed be due to lack of care in keeping out stray fields. My own laboratory is in a windowless below-ground basement, but that is not sufficient on its own to keep out radio signals, as I can confirm simply by switching on my radio set.

We have come a long way since Galvani's chance observation of a twitching frog's leg, and though much research still lies ahead before one can say for sure how organic morphology works, or why we might be affected by electromagnetic fields, there are some glimmerings of light through the tunnel, with the physicist and the cellular biologist dimly able to discern each other peering down opposite ends.

Italy is not only among the first runners in the physics of organic life. It is also well up in the race to develop electro-healing. Another team from Modena's Institute of Normal Human Anatomy, headed by Dr Vittoria Ottani, has been trying to see if pulsed ELF magnetic fields can speed up wound healing.

Bone Healing

Robert Becker had devoted many decades to showing not only that direct currents emanate from wounds as they heal (this had been known as early as 1860, and even in Volta's time) but that by applying a current in the right direction the healing process could be accelerated. In the early 1960s he was working with Andrew Bassett of Columbia University when they first found that an externally applied voltage stimulated the growth of bone in a dog's tibia.

The best current strength appeared to be 5-50 microamps, below which there was no effect, while stronger currents induced necrosis and gross tissue destruction. It was also important to deliver the current properly: by using a silver wire with a DC cathode electrode, significantly less current was necessary. Even infected non-union fractures could be successfully treated in this way. The FDA approved some of the new techniques (both the pulsed coil method and the percutaneous method) with surprising alacrity. Becker's method involved surgical exposure, so took a little longer, even though it used less current (0.1 to 5 microamps).

At the beginning of the 1970s, reports were appearing from researchers like L. S. Levine and D. D. Levy, who found that pulsed EM energy induced bone growth in many ways. J. D. Jacobs and co-workers applied the same techniques to periodontal defects. In 1977 Andy Bassett and Arthur Pilla were reporting 'inoperative salvage of non-unions' (they meant repair of unmendable bones without any operations). Through the 1980s Smith and Nagel, Wahlstrom, Haupt, Fontanesi, and other researchers had already reported positive results after applying pulsed ELF fields to ununited bone fractures (fractures where the shattered bone simply will not re-unite).

Wound Healing

The application of EM fields to wounds, to see if they heal faster, has been a favourite research subject, not only using direct current, but also with higher frequencies. One of the earliest modern experiments was done in 1975. Instead of using power frequencies, Shaposhnikov and his Soviet co-workers applied microwaves at $4000 \mu W/cm^2$ to guinea pigs whose backs had been subjected to a five cm wound. Microscopic examination after eleven days showed that the exposed wounds were in a more advanced state of healing, and this was confirmed by the rather horrendous procedure of seeing how much more force was needed to re-open them: from 30 per cent to 72 per cent more mechanical strain had to be applied to the exposed group to break open the wound again.

The first *ever* account of organic regeneration was by Spallanzini in 1768. The contribution of electromagnetism to regeneration however, was only realized in 1909, when O. E. Frazee was researching the effects of direct electrical current stimulation on frogs and salamanders. He passed the current through the water in which they were kept, and found to his amazement that this seemed to increase the salamander's rate of limb regeneration.

After this, two other scientists – Harold Saxton Burr from Yale, and J. Lund from the University of Texas – carried out many experiments and found that applying similar currents to plants and other animals also increased their growth. Unfortunately, their work was largely ignored at the time by the scientific community, who thought that it was simply the product of instrumental artifacts.

In a now famous set of experiments in 1952, Marsh and Beams showed that regeneration of a flatworm could be altered by applying a direct current, even to the extent that the severed creature would begin to grow two heads, and that as the current strength was increased the tail would grow where the head had been!

The direction of the DC current was vital, since reversing the direction actually slowed up the growth process. It had been observed (by Humphrey and Seal) that rapidly growing tissues were electrically negative in polarity, with tumours being the most negatively charged of all. So Humphrey and Seal first implanted malignant tumours in rats, and then attached copper or zinc anodes over the tumour masses and applied a 2 milliAmp current for three hours a day.

In tests on 18 cases, the volume of the tumours in the controls was 7 times greater – the rats all died within 31 days – while seven of the treated animals showed complete regression, and were still alive twelve months later. In a 1962 *Science* article, Huggins and Yang showed conclusively that carcinogenic agents produced their deadly effects by their capacity for electron transfer: the connection between electromagnetism and cancer was now staring the scientific community in the face.

But simple current flow did not by itself explain the healing process, as Becker realized:

On the basis of these observations we theoretically divided regeneration into two separate but sequential phases: the first being the formation of a blastema [new young cellular growth] in response to a signal that is stimulating to the local cells and through their dedifferentiation produces the blastema. The information content of the signal responsible for the first phase is obviously sparse and may be correspondingly simple, whereas the signal responsible for the second phase must be capable of carrying an enormous amount of information (what structure is to be formed, what its orientation with respect to the rest of the body is to be and finally all the details of its complex structure).

In our view, the DC potentials and currents generated at the site of injury by the DC control system were quite suitable as the signal for the first phase, whereas their information content was totally inadequate for the second phase. This concept meant there could be two mechanisms at fault in those animals normally incapable of regenerative growth. First the initial phase may fail to reproduce a blastema because of either an inadequate signal or an inability of the cells to respond to an adequate signal by dedifferentiation.

If an adequate blastema was formed, the second phase informational signal might be missing or inadequate to produce the subsequent redifferentiation and growth. Since it is common knowledge that non-regenerating animals fail in the first phase and do not produce blastema, and in view of our findings of the polarity differences between generators and non-regenerators in the first phase, we postulated that the initial stimulating signal was missing in the non-regenerating animals. Stimulation of this signal by external means was technically quite feasible; however, one could not predict whether the cells would be capable of responding to it or if they did, and a blastema was formed, whether the complex informational signal that controlled the second phase would be present.

What Becker perhaps failed to realize was that embedded in the current flow – that is the flow of ions towards the wound – was an electromagnetic signal carrying all information necessary for regeneration and orientation of the individual cells. Furthermore, it seems from other research into negative ions that the signal can only be carried by negative ion flow, not positive.

Even so, Becker was very close when he said:

It would now appear fairly certain that the specific sequence of changes in electrical potential that produce regenerative growth are themselves produced by the neuro-epidermal junction, and not by either the nerves or the epidermis alone. Intrinsic electromagnetic energy inherent in the nervous system of the body is therefore the factor that exerts the major controlling influence over growth processes in general. The nerves, acting in concert with some electrical factor of the epidermis, produce the specific sequence of electrical changes that cause limb regenerative growth. In animals not normally capable of regeneration this specific sequence of electrical changes is absent. However, it can be stimulated by artificial means, resulting in blastema formation and major regenerative growth even in mammals.

Because all electrons by their nature carry a negative charge, they will only be able to travel towards an attractive (and opposite) polarity. So these messengers, in flowing in their millions down any conductive filament – or as EM fields through free space – convey the information necessary to initiate DNA synthesis of the relevant new cells. Whether by conduction or by induction through action at a distance is almost irrelevant, provided the vital messages get through.

This is why the polarities in healing wounds are as they are, a phenomenon which Becker reported, but could not explain. The number of ions flowing when a current passes down a filament, or as a field through space is enormous: in the trillions per second. During the healing process, cells near the wound first dedifferentiate, that is they lose their specialist characteristics. Then they redifferentiate into the required special form needed for the wounded area. This process can happen so fast in salamanders that they can even repair wounds to the heart and survive before their blood runs away through the hole. If we could achieve the same effects by external assistance to our own serious wounds, this would be truly a pinacle of electro-healing.

In one of his most telling remarks, Becker points out that all cells carry the complete genetic programme or genome: thus the nucleus of a muscle cell, for example, has the genome for muscle unrepressed and operating and the genomes for all the other cell types are present but repressed. The genome produces the specialized cell type by governing the production of specific proteins which make up the cell itself. Dedifferentiation consists of de-repressing these repressed genomes so the cell returns to a more primitive, less differentiated level and now has the option to re-differentiate into a new cell type, depending on its local circumstances. The control of that process can be conducted or induced by electromagnetic means.

Pulsed magnetic fields by themselves are found to enhance human DNA synthesis, according to Abe Liboff, one of the original proponents, with Charles Polk, of the idea of ion cyclotron resonance as the mechanism by which EM fields act on living cells. His research was inevitably confined to test-tube studies, since experiments on living human beings are strictly controlled, even though we are all taking part in a massive biological experiment simply by living in any house with electric wiring!

With this body of accumulated research to guide her, Vittoria Ottani tried in 1988 to see what happened when she made a 3 cm-square skin wound on the backs of four-month old rats, then exposed the unfortunate creatures for some 30 minutes every 12 hours to PEMFs. (The pulse was a positive triangle at 50 Hertz, with a peak of 8 milliTesla). At six, twelve, twenty-one, and forty-two days the progress of the wound was evaluated, using light and electron microscopy.

At the end of the 42 days the PEMF-treated rats had healed completely, while the control group still lacked 6 per cent of the wound surface to be covered. The same stage had been reached by the exposed rats 21 days earlier. Moreover the treated rats showed earlier cellular organization, collagen formation and other signs of healing.

Ottani concluded that she and her co-workers had succeeded where others failed because she had used slightly different frequencies and treatment duration, though precisely which parameters were responsible is still a mystery. There may have even been some other factor – a lower general background EM environment for example – not taken into account.

One might wonder whether any research into PEMFs is being carried out in the United Kingdom. A joint team from Guy's and St Bartholomew's hospitals in London, under the leadership of Mary Dyson, is doing so. She presented some of their research results at a conference in Birmingham in May 1990. She and her colleagues showed that the exposure of certain cells to particular wavelengths of visible light and low energy infra-red irradiation can increase the release of growth factors which stimulate healing processes.

Meanwhile, Tiina Karu in Russia and Anton Kranmer in Austria have shown that Helium-Ne lasers and ordinary red light (which is really electromagnetic radiation with a wavelength of 633 nanometres) could also stimulate DNA synthesis, and cell proliferation, while at St Bartholomew's Hospital in London, Richard Dixey and Glen Rein have detected that nerve cells can be persuaded to release noradrenaline by exposing them to pulsed magnetic fields. (I discuss the effects of light in Chapter 4.)

Encouraged by these and similar research results, let us examine now what magneto-therapeutic products are already available and what are the claims of their distributors.

Magneto-therapy's armory is beginning to be vast. It can be conveniently divided into two classes: the products which claim to protect from unwanted intrusive fields and so allow the body to restore itself or not to fall ill in the first place; and the products which assist and encourage the repair process or reduce existing pain.

Since I have already dealt with protective measures in my book *Electropollution* (Thorsons 1990) I have confined my brief catalogue to the second class, which is by no means exhaustive. These can also be divided into two: active devices, which actually deliver some kind of signal, be it magnetic (static or alternating) or electromagnetic (direct or alternating current induced signals), and passive devices, which do no more than amplify the fields existing around them.

Active devices

Delta Key

This device is worn like a watch, similar to the Teslar watch, Mekos, or the Biomag, all of which emit low frequency magnetic pulses, just like an ordinary quartz watch, though at different self-adjustable frequencies. The Delta Key goes a step further, however. It was developed in 1979 by Stephen Walpole after he had sustained a bad car accident which left him immobilized and suffering from severe migraines. When analysing his own brain rhythms (he was an electronics engineer) he found that they differed from normal rhythms in that certain frequencies appeared to be missing. The Delta Key, powered by a 3 volt battery, aims to replace these by ELF pulses of the missing frequencies. Its Norfolk-based manufacturers have developed and patented the device with the help of Sanyo, who also make it under licence. Other disorders said to be treatable with the Delta Key are arthritis, M.E., insomnia, multiple sclerosis, and back-ache. Each person's missing frequencies may be different, so the Delta

Key has to be individually tuned to emit the necessary lacunae by means of a brain-scanner. The Delta Key is available only on loan against a refundable deposit. This approach to electro-healing seems most promising, in the light of my researches into cerebral morphogenetic radiation.

Electrosleep

This concept is designed to produce sleep by applying different frequencies of AC electromagnetic energy to the brain by means of small electrodes. Though used to assist the patient to sleep while undergoing surgical operations, it is said to have other psychological applications. The technique seems very much at the experimental stage, and to originate from the early work of Aldani. I have no other information, and would need a lot more evidence before trying it myself! A device of this kind is marketed by Healthguard UK, of Manchester.

H.E.T. (Home Electronic Therapy) Ltd

This North London-based firm makes a range of instruments, including a muscle and joint manipulator which, in combination with its patented rigid activated splint system, transmits a VLF pulsed magnetic field to damaged or rheumatoid joints. The same firm have also developed a dual head magnetic cell tissue re-animator, generating 4, 10, and 14 Hertz to the wound area. Finally, their Quadrapulse machine is used to stimulate muscles at the same frequencies, with an adjustable (0-800 A/m) magnetic field strength. Up to 36 electrodes can be operated simultaneously.

Magmende

This range of machines delivers PEMF to alleviate a very wide range of conditions, from arthritis, bone and muscle injuries, to bronchial and respiratory problems. There are four choices of frequency, modulation, and intensity. It is distributed by the firm of the same name in Ilminster, Somerset.

The Magnetodent

This consists of a revolving glass tube containing magnetized salts. The tube, powered by a battery, is held against the cheek and stroked down it. The objective is to degauss the metal fillings in the mouth, so that dental decay and mouth pain are reduced. I have not tested this equipment so have no opinion on its efficacy. The same firm also offer a Magnetomat, a device which applies electric currents to food which is said thereby to be freed of toxic influences.

Myolift-S

This device aims to improve skin quality, tightening and rejuvenating the appearance of the face and body. Its manufacturers, Medizintechnik Keller GmbH of Langenfeld, Germany, claim that after treatment patients can look up to fifteen years younger. (I haven't tried it myself, for some reason!) The device uses eight 1.5 volt batteries to deliver a micro-amp current via a computer controlled instrument. 'At most you will feel a pleasant tingling', they state. Special frequencies are said to mobilize cellulite, causing the elimination of metabolic residues. The product is distributed in the Europe by The Natural Clinic Promotion Centre of Tunbridge Wells.

Noma Super 4

Manufactured by S. L. Electronics of Weybridge, and supplied by P.H. Medical, this device provides a choice of waveforms and frequencies ranging from 0–100 and 1–1000 Hz, and with a fixed pulse width of 0.5 or 0.05 milliseconds. It includes a digital frequency display, and electro-healing may be applied via rubber electrodes (for transcutaneous nerve stimulation) or a lightweight headset for auricular therapy. There are also crocodile clip leads for electro-acupuncture.

The Reharmonizer

This does not seem by itself to contain any magnetic element. However it consists of a tiny sealed phial of water which it is claimed has been magnetized and vibrated prior to sale, but no further details are available to me of what exactly has been done. I would not go so far as to say that it is ineffective, but it seems a variant on a homoeopathic remedy which I discuss on p. 98.

PEME (Pulsed Electromagnetic Energy) at Bluestone-Ling Clinic

This is a machine pioneered since 1972 by Kay Kiernan, whose clients include members of the royal family, well-known actors, sportspeople, and dancers. It is used mainly for the treatment of soft tissue injuries to joints and ligaments, haemophiliac arthropathy and bone healing, but the descriptive literature lists 33 different applications, including migraine. It is also claimed to reduce the pain associated with these ailments.

I have known Kay, whose youthful appearance belies her 70 years (she uses the machine herself on a regular basis for rejuvenation), as a tireless delegate at many conferences and exhibitions of complementary medicine, and have always been impressed by her humility and sincerity, often in the face of stark disbelief concerning her methods. She would be the first to admit she does not know how her PEME machines work, but can always produce a sheaf of testimonials.

It would be nice to have the machines tested in rigorous case control situations, to see if they compare favourably with the Ottani and other studies. The machine's frequency can be adjusted between 8 and 800 pulses per second, though I do not have any further characteristics of the pulses used.

The Portic Electronic Bandage

This device was developed by a British researcher, Dr Richard Bentall, working at Maryland University's Technology Advancement Program. It is a radiofrequency emitter, disposable after three weeks' use, and incorporates an antenna attached to a battery-driven source. Clinical trials on rats seem to indicate a net 18 per cent improvement in wound healing time. The trials encountered difficulty because the rats kept scraping the plastic bandages off, but modifications should ensure a useful evaluation eventually.

The WeiKang Electromembrane
(electronic antiphlogistic and analgesic membrane – EAAM – also called Electro-Acupad)

This material, which looks like a gauze bandage, is claimed to contain negative ions. Applying the membrane is said to relieve pain, and promote the healing of skeleto-muscular disorders. It is said to retard the skin's ageing process, inhibit toxic pollution, and to combat the effects of stress.

The material itself is produced out of 'a water-repelling texture with extremely low electrical conductivity, and extremely high tendency towards separation of charge during smallest movements. It is charged on both sides with a high negative charge which discharges itself slowly and continuously on the skin.' Accordingly, if two Weikang membranes are placed together they repel each other, because they are of the same polarity. Its negative charge can also, it is claimed, pull positive ions ('such as mercury') out of the skin.

The electromembrane was invented by Professor Sun Caoming of the Applied Chemistry Laboratory (Chemical Engineering Dept) of Beijing Institute of Technology. It is now manufactured by a US company, Energetic Research Inc. of Los Angeles, and won a gold medal at the 25th Brussels Eureka World Fair in 1985 for industrial innovation. In Britain it is marketed by Villain Ltd of Glasgow.

Writing in English in a medical digest published by the Institute of Chinese Herbs (based surprisingly not in China but in Irvine, Los Angeles), Dr Pi-Kwang Tsung in 1989 explained the rationale behind the invention:

The human body is composed of innumerable cells, every one of which is enveloped in a cell membrane. A cell lives by absorbing nutritive elements and discharging waste through the membrane. A cell is positively charged on the outside and negatively charged on the inside, so when negative ions decrease and positive ions increase, the absorption of nutritional elements and the discharge of waste becomes more difficult. This causes poor metabolism, leading to weaker physiological functions, possibly causing illness.

(I shall be discussing the effects of ions in another chapter.)
Negative ions are called anions and positive ones cations. The Weikang membrane induces anions into the body in order to attain the optimal systemic effect on the vital bodily fluids. As Dr Tsung says:

Human blood is normally slightly alkaline with a pH [hydrogen potential] value of around of 7.4. However, those substances which generate energy in the human body are mostly acidic, such as cereals, meat, and fish. When anions increase, the amount of sodium and calcium ions in the blood increases, turning acidic blood into slightly alkaline blood. Moreover, gamma globulin (a kind of immune protein) in the blood increases with the incremental increase of anions. This immune protein can help to fight disease.

The material underwent four years of clinical trials, involving 600 patients at the Union and five other hospitals at Beijing, with an effective claimed success rate of 90 per cent. The cases included such ailments as skin allergy (80 per cent improvement in four days), tendinitis following shoulder dislocation (100 per cent improvement in six days), and acne (70 per cent improvement in six days); many types of sprain were also reported to have been considerably relieved. These percentages sound impressive, but the way they are derived means that a chance result would be rated as a 50 per cent success rate in the manufacturers rating system. Even so, in a table showing their results, only in 6 cases out of 100 was the membrane totally ineffective, whereas there was a complete recovery in 29 cases. This too is somewhat suspect, since we do not know how many of the cases would have recovered normally anyway.

In another table of results (this time from 200 cases) in 33 cases (16.5 per cent) the treatment was ineffective. Looking at selected cases presented to Dr W. Greene of Houston is also impressive, but again there are no controls against which to judge comparative success. This is the problem with quoting uncontrolled results. The promoters of EAAM are not short of explanations as to how it works: 'Anionic therapy appears to achieve pain relief by enhancing the production of endogenous opiates,' states Dr Tsung, and certainly there is evidence from the work of Dr Cyril Smith at Salford University's Department of Electric Engineeering that these endogenous opiates can indeed be induced by electromagnetic energy. Moreover, as early as 1965, R. Melzack and P. D. Wall reported in *Science*, a reputable journal, that the preferential activation of large efferent nerve fibres would inhibit the transmission of painful impulses.

Another explanation apart from this one is offered for the efficacy of EAAM: the promoters claim that EAAM has the effect of increasing the local blood circulation, diminishing swelling and promoting fracture healing. Its original Chinese patent was approved by 18 medical experts whose report in December 1985 confirmed that it was remarkably effective in improving fracture healing, alleviation of pain from angina pectoris, and speeded up wound repair generally.

Passive Devices

The instruments above are active, that is to say they actually create magnetic or electromagnetic fields and apply them in one way or another to the body. The second class of device does not have any energetic component of its own, and because of this is regarded with much suspicion, particularly since such devices have no moving parts. In fact all things move, as one early Greek philosopher-scientist put it, though he was probably unaware of the random Brownian motion of molecules in any fluid, or that all atoms include spinning electrons. A magnet does not 'move', but we know that because of its net magnetic moment from the aligned spin direction of its electrons that it can exert a force, sometimes a very powerful one.

Other arrangements of molecules can actually amplify the energies arriving into them. A crystal is a good example, and these were used in the earliest kind of radio sets (called crystal sets, for precisely that reason). Against that background it may not seem so strange that passive devices can also exert influences, given that we all give off an electromagnetic signal corresponding to the structured unique design of our DNA within the chromosomes of our nucleated cells. It would appear then that the mechanism of these passive devices is simply to augment or amplify the body's own signal and thereby improve its signal-to-noise ratio.

Having said all this, there are some devices which incorporate both elements, using the principle that all aerial receivers are also, *per se*, transmitters. One of the earliest of all such devices was of this hybrid variety, though at the time it completely baffled its investigators. It was called the oscilloclast.

The Oscilloclast

Dr Albert Abrams' 'Oscilloclast' was a strange device which he claimed could produce 'some electrical phenomenon which appeared to be non-specific in its clinical effects'. The withering report in the *British Medical Journal* of 26 January 1924 condemned this instrument as an 'electrical toy', and said its rheostats 'would be thrown out of any high-school laboratory'. A more detailed analysis was made by Messrs Ackermann and Clark of Westminster, London, about the same time, and they too were clearly sceptical and baffled:

As far as we are able to judge, and considering it purely from the point of view of physics, we are of the opinion that no consistent, trustworthy, or physically and logically explainable results can be obtained; and that consequently such physical phenomena as there may be in connection with the Abrams method of diagnosis as we know it are perfectly useless for any purpose.

Whew! Nor did they think that a collection of rheostats (resistance coils) 'could be an advantage for measuring small amounts of ohmic resistance'.

However, they noted a small leakage current through the subject, which was interrupted 196 times per minute (3.2 times per second, the same frequency as theta waves from the brain, the waves of paradoxical sleep). Since Hans Berger had not yet announced to the world his astounding discovery of pulsed rhythms issuing from the brain, the significance of this pulse repetition rate was completely lost on the investigators. Nor at that time had Penfield mapped the cortex to find from which places in the brain the polarized Great pyramidal cells emitted these motor and sensory signals via the corpus callosum. Broadcast radio program transmission itself was a mere four years old.

'A rough or vibratory sensation at the points of the fingers was unmistakeable' when the subject was stroked or when the investigator held the terminal in his teeth. 'The patient is undoubtedly subjected to some electrical environment when under treatment, but we repeat that it is not our province to conjecture what therapeutic effect, for good or ill, would thereby be occasioned.' However, since their investigation was 'not extended into the domain of molecular physics *per se*', they 'could not perform a critical judgement from an electronic point of view'.

Such conclusions were hardly surprising. Yet the oscilloclast was clearly delivering a pulsed electromagnetic field (PEMF) to its patient, which though, as Abrams saw, was non-specific, helped convey the signals of the brain to the body, thereby acting as a carrier wave. The construction of the oscillator is such that it must also have been creating a signal at very high radio frequencies, though what the rheostats were designed to do is still a mystery to me. At a guess they may have helped the apparatus to amplify the very specific frequencies coming from the patient. In this regard then the instrument combined an active carrier wave with a passive device which could detect and amplify the patients own unique frequency.

Around the same time George W. Crile wrote in his book *A Bipolar Theory of Living Processes*:

It is clear that cellular radiation produces the electrical current which operates adaptively in the organism as a whole, producing memory, reason, imagination, emotion, special senses, secretion, muscular action, response to infection, normal growth, and the growth of tumours and cancers – all of which are governed adaptively by the electrical charges that are generated by the shortwave or ionising radiation in the protoplasm.

Almost 20 years later Ivan G. McDaniel referred to 'biological wave systems, vibratory and interconnecting by nature, which tend to hold together a part or organ for the purpose of fulfilling its specific function'.

As one French doctor put it:

The confirmation of the results obtained from the Hertzian waves, combined with the non-aggression of this therapy, grant an extremely precious procedure in the field of biotherapeutic medicine: this is of a non-polluting machine which respects man in his entirety and in his complexity.

Biocrystal Pulsors
These are purely passive devices, being plastic discs about half an inch thick and an inch and a half across in which are said to be sealed microcrystals. The pulsors are of three types: red,

green, and blue, and they are variously said to energize or relax
the body. They are claimed to have three frequencies.

The pulsors seem fearfully expensive, but their proponents
in the United Kingdom, Misa Halu and Zbynek Zahalka, have
been selling them successfully for years at complementary
medicine exhibitions, though the devices themselves are made
in the United States by Dr George Yao. Yao claims recent
annual sales of $2 million for his pulsors, without advertising.
I have tried them but with no detectable effect. The claims for
pulsors are that they amplify the biomagnetic field of the body
two or three times, and 'block the flow of any negative energy
from therapist to patient . . . changing and amplifying
vibrations of places and people'.

The pulsor apparently 'removes the charge from electrons,
converting them into neutrinos which will have no further
effects on the biophysical energy systems of the human body'.
A friend of mine who is a physicist would be very interested
to know that since he has been looking for neutrinos with
some exceedingly expensive equipment for some years!

Yao claims to have been a chemical and aerospace engineer
working on the problems of satellite protection from electromagnetic radiation. Given that background one might have
expected a more technical explanation of the mechanism by
which they are claimed to work. But there are no clinical trials,
not even attributed testimonials – hardly very convincing.

The Cosmoton

I mentioned this passive device briefly in *Electropollution*. This
blue-gold medallion or pendant is 4.5 cm in circumference,
constructed with 'multiple pure gold and pure silver, and was
selling at about £48. It is German in origin, from Ordo-Stiftung
of Kanstanz-Wallhausen, but is marketed in Britain by Mrs H.
Pickles of Leeds.

The Cosmoton's distributors offer a good deal more
information than most promoters of such wares. 'It con-
centrates the vital forces of the Cosmos within and beams
them out to the wearer,' says the sales literature. It is said to
help infants, to harmonize radiations from TVs, considerably
improve the quality of food when the device is left on a
refrigerator or deep freezer, and never requires any
maintenance or re-energizing.

The literature is contradictory: its benefits only come with time, so expect no immediate results, it says. However, 'the golden radiation symbol should be worn in the heart region, with the symbol pointing outwards . . . If the effect is found to be too intense it can be controlled by wrapping tinfoil round it once or twice.' One may place a pendant on the electricity meter, one is told, in which case it screens off the electric system off the house.

In the Cosmoton literature a curious scientific experiment is described (though its origin in any peer-reviewed scientific literature is not given). In 1930 the Pfeiffer-Kollisko research team placed the salts of seven non-ferrous metals in separate test-tubes and inserted an absorbent paper in each. As the solutions rose up the paper they formed specific patterns. Whenever the moon occulted a planet, thus preventing the planet's radiations from reaching the test tubes, one of the salt patterns would collapse. For example, when Venus was occulted only the copper pattern collapsed. When Mars was occulted only the iron pattern collapsed. When Jupiter was occulted the tin pattern was affected. The others are not given, but after the occultation had passed the patterns were said to re-establish themselves.

This is at least a solidly observed phenomenon, if true. It should be replicable – that is to say we should be able to repeat it at any time, and if it is always found to happen, we have perhaps found out something very important: that planetary influences can be proved to have a terrestrial effect, and that they are linked with specific metals in some way. From there are the beginnings of credibility for devices like the Cosmoton, and indeed for astrology itself.

Paracelsus, the fifteenth-century physician, went further than the research team. He linked these metals to specific organs of the body. Inside the Cosmoton's cellulose (reconstituted wood) case are seven oscillating circuits arranged in the same sequence as the planets are with respect to the sun. These are said to absorb and transmit cosmic radiations in the same way as the salts were said to be affected.

At least we are now beginning to get onto firmer, testable ground. I never exclude devices such as these out of hand, but the correlation between such phenomena – if they are real – and the body's organs and their health, is not yet properly explained by this discovery. It should at least be testable though, and the results should be confirmed or not, rather than being left to the mysterious 1930 research team, or to the writings of a medieval philosopher-scientist.

Displec

This creation of John Crow, who now lives in Norfolk, takes two forms: (a) a lapel badge worn as an adornment and (b) a sticker badge to be adhered to computers or to any other EMF-emitting appliances. I have no further information, and its originator admits 'it is difficult to quantify the benefits to be acquired by the use of Displec,' but quotes unattributed testimonials. The only technical information is that it is 'based on a complex technology and a specific numeric equation'. He also calls it a calculating stone, and his inspiration for Displec seems to come from a novel *Xorandor*, by Christine Brook-Rose. Faced with this sort of product claim I am not surprised that physicians and medical practitioners alike find the whole concept of 'subtle energy medicine' beneath critical attention.

The Nuclear Receptor

This passive device is of German origin, being made by Johannes Fisslinger of Munich, but sold in the United Kingdom for £98. It is a medallion about 3.5 cm in diameter and consists of 'special metals' and a 24-carat gold plating.

By the use of a parabolic [curved] lens the Nuclear Receptor traps microwaves, radiation, psychic vibrations, or any disharmonic energies, and filters exponentially into harmonious forms of energy by the correct positioning of 144 mini-pyramid shaped filters located on its surface. The positioning sequence corresponds to what is called the Fibonacci (Phi) Curve. These energies are reflected to one of nine different gemstones on the focus point of the lens which then sends the currents into the aura of the wearer.

I must admit I'm not much the wiser for this explanation. The gemstones are listed, together with their reputedly associated glands and bodily functions, as well as 'the body vibratory rate of DNA' (energizing, maintaining or tranquillizing).

Family of Receptor Vibratory Patterns

COLOUR	white	red	orange	yellow	green	blue	violet
SYNTHETIC GEMSTONE	zirkonium	ruby	garnet	citron, peridot	emerald	aquamarine blue sapphire	amethyst
ENDOCRINE GLAND	pineal	pituitary	adrenal	liver, kidney	thyroid	heart, thymus	gonads, sexual
BODILY FUNCTION AFFECTED	meditation, attitude	circulation, energy	weight control, energy	detoxification, fluid balance	weight, metabolism, balance, heart circ.	immune system	sexual drive, creativity
BODY VIBRATORY RATE OF DNA	▲	▲	▶	▶	▶	▼	▼

▲ – up, energizing ▶ – maintain, balancing ▼ – down, tranquillizing

The nuclear receptor can be acquired in nine different frequencies – presumably one has to spend about £900 to get complete coverage of the entire endocrine system. Its manufacturers' claims for the nuclear receptor are somewhat vague: 'Tests have shown that the nuclear receptor exerts a balancing and invigorating influence on the body when it is exposed to harmful environmental pollution or stress.' It has the ability 'to synthesize toxic or disharmonious forms of energy into components known as electrical precursors, which aid the body in all forms of metabolism.'

There do not appear to be any polarizing elements in the medallion, nor are there any sources (except Brad Steiger the science fiction writer, and a Dr Fred Bell) quoted for the correlations shown in the table above. The nuclear receptor probably looks quite pretty though.

The Rayma Biomagnetic Regulator

This passive device is a metallic bracelet of Spanish manufacture, silver-gold or gold-plated, with a gap and metal bobbles on each end. It is said to be made of a polarized electrolytic material, which would probably apply to any metal bar, including the average horseshoe, all of which form open oscillating circuits.

When worn on the left wrist it is claimed to influence the brain's beta rhythms where 'an imbalance can lead to heart disorders, varicose veins, hypertension, and painful menstruation' (no evidence of these correlations are given). When worn on the right wrist the bracelet is said to influence the alpha rhythms, where an imbalance 'can lead to depression, tension, stress, anxiety mental and physical fatigue, lumbago, insomnia, headaches, and arthritic or rheumatic symptoms'. Again no correlating evidence is offered. What happens when you have both types of symptom at the same time is not explained, though a further claim is that the Rayma 'has given relief to millions in Europe'.

The device is presumably some sort of open oscillating circuit, very much like a small version of the horseshoe, which is said to bring good luck. A horseshoe would oscillate at about the frequency of hydrogen, but this device, being smaller, would oscillate at much higher frequencies. The price is about £20 to £30 and it is marketed by Runcheck of Chester. It is claimed to absorb the body's positive ions. I have some belief that this sort of device might help to amplify cerebral signals, but it may not be more efficacious than the copper half bracelets one finds worn to relieve rheumatism, which cost considerably less. As an adornment however, the Rayma seems quite attractive.

All of these treatments sound a little zany. They often give little if any technical detail, which must infuriate any serious scientific researcher. I would guess that Magnes had similar difficulties in persuading his fellow Greeks that his stone could attract metal until they actually saw it happening. Chinese navigators who first found that the needle always pointed south must also have been initially quite nervous of trusting it on the world's oceans. But magnetism, static or pulsed, is not the only electromagnetic energy which affects us. Visible light is also electromagnetic energy, and in the next chapter you will see that it can also have important effects on organic life.

4. The Light of Life

From earliest times an ordered system was in operation; a
system which was a non-material force, controlling everything.

St John's Gospel, 1.1.

The first chapter of the Gospel according to St John the Divine
refers to light. When, in the time of King James, scholars
translated the New Testament from ancient Greek to English
(it had already undergone one transition from Hebrew), they
faithfully copied every word. As a result the English version
of this chapter has come down to us as gibberish, beautiful
but unintelligible, and is now intoned uncomprehendingly by
millions during our annual Christmas carol festivals.

What the apostle was trying to explain – struggling to
describe concepts which were totally unknown to his audience
– was that all organic life relies on electromagnetic energy for
its sustenance. True, the greek *logos* does mean 'word'. But it
is also the derivation of 'logic' and law, any ordered system in
fact. Yes, *en arche* means 'in the beginning', as in archaeology.
But it also can mean 'in control', like arch-bishop or arch-
tyrant. For the Greeks of those days, moreover, although *theos*
meant God, their gods were the spirits of almost any material
thing, living or non-living. So they would have gods of the
trees, of water, or even of the theatre. 'God' was their word for
any non-material force or permeating spirit.

When John was talking about light (*phos*, from which we get
photography or photons) he meant not only the visible light
which we can perceive, but also the entirety of the
electromagnetic spectrum, a concept originally derived from
the Pythagoreans, who must have got their knowledge from

even further west than Sicily where they were established. This is why he talks about 'the light that shines in darkness' – it was his way of saying 'electromagnetic energy outside the visible spectrum', and a very elegant way of expressing it, too. Today we sometimes refer to ultraviolet radiation as 'black light'.

Finally, the Greek word *egeneto* certainly means 'was made'. But it really means 'was born' or 'became alive'. So when John says that without this light (that shines in darkness) 'nothing was made that was made', he means that without it nothing could become alive: he was distinguishing electromagnetic man from lifeless materials. Now take another look at St John's first chapter: the light which lighteth every man coming into the world is his way of describing the electromagnetic fields which distinguish and maintain our morphology.

One of our most inalienable human needs is light. For organic plants it is an essential, for without photosynthesis the average green plant turns white and ultimately atrophies. Without sunlight and the vitamin D it synthesizes we get rickets (osteomalacia in adults). At the bottom of some oceans, it is true, some creatures lead a completely dark life and the average earthworm trapped above ground will expire through exposure to ultraviolet radiation. But for human beings light is vital.

Through evolution we have developed sensors to a very small part indeed of the electromagnetic spectrum, the only part, with few exceptions like 'radar hearing' to which we are not completely deaf. (This is not strictly true, since dowsers have shown that human beings are capable of sensing very small static magnetic fields by moving through them, and some people are said to be sensitive to power frequency electric fields, though the evidence is far from clear: I once tested a so-called electrical sensitive and found that she still reacted when I only pretended to turn on the current). Finally we may also be more sensitive than we realize to other EM frequencies, if the researches of Albert Abrams, Ruth Drown, W. E. Boyd, and Hans Berger are true.

Even so, the wealth of information available to us from the tiny range of frequencies (760 to 380 nanometre waves) which span the colours of visible light is staggering: we are capable of distinguishing not just the seven colours of the rainbow but very many shades and nuances in between, each of which may be only a few nanometres wavelength different from its neighbour.

As for intensity, it was reliably shown by von Helmholtz in the nineteenth century that the human eye is capable of discerning one single photon of light in total darkness at one extreme, and the direct brightness of the sun at the other. Our sensitivity to the smallest movement is good, though considerably surpassed by some animals and most birds, while hawks have resolution which can distinguish a corn-field vole from hundreds of feet in the air. No single electronic instrument has such a capability in such a small space as our eye and brain, despite all the advances in satellite reconnaisance and radio and light telescopy.

Apart from these wonders, visible light and its near neighbour ultraviolet light have much more important effects on our health than were believed just a few decades ago, both for better and for worse. Of these perhaps the most interesting discoveries concern the impact of light on the serotonin-melatonin hormones released by the pineal gland in the brain. (The gland is a pea-sized object, shaped like a pine cone, hence its name.) The anatomy of the nervous pathways affecting this gland has been fairly well mapped: where the optic nerves from the retinas cross over at the optic chiasma (so as to balance their radiative effect on the brain and give us depth vision) there is a small cluster of neurones called the suprachiasmatic nuclei. From these pass efferents to the pineal gland which can thereby sense whether or not there are light signals passing down the optic nerves. (There are other indirect pathways to the pineal, via the hypothalamus and spinal cord). It is possible also that the pineal itself is directly sensitive to light (it has been called the third eye). In birds for example, the pineal is situated right next to the skull at the fontanelle. The question is, can it distinguish between the natural light's frequency and wavelength from all the other EM energy – radio frequencies, for example – to which we are all exposed nowadays?

In response to light the pineal starts to secrete melatonin (it is the only gland which is capable of doing this). When the light increases, the pineal secretes serotonin instead. The former, melatonin, has an inhibitory effect on the body's sensitivity to light (and other forms of EM energy) and thus it acts to assist sleep onset, thereby increasing the body's lethargy, even to the point of depression. The latter, serotonin, seems to do the reverse.

'Melatonin' comes from the Greek word for 'black', and its derivatives are associated with pigmentation of the skin – dark skin is more capable of resisting the sun's radiation than fair (unpigmented) skin, which is why there are so many Scandinavians in Madeira at Christmas rather than in July. Albinos, who are completely devoid of pigmentation, have no melanin-producing capacity.

Tampering with the natural light-dark cycle, by introducing artificial lighting in winter for example, seems to produce a syndrome known as Seasonal Affective Disorder (SAD). This may have always existed to some extent, to judge from accounts of melancholia (which is so called because it was thought to result from a surfeit of black bile, and not that far wrong either) during the middle ages. But modern electric light in the winter evenings, and extended TV watching, seem to have exacerbated its effect. At the beginning of this century about 75 per cent of workers worked outdoors, as compared to less than 10 per cent today, so we are all more likely to work under artificial light than ever before.

Russell Reiter and Alfred Lewy have been exploring ways to defeat SAD. In 1980, while working with the National Institutes of Mental Health, Lewy found that bright light reduced melatonin levels, and by exposing patients to bright artificial light early in the morning he was able to correct the phase shift which they had incurred, so relieving their depression – a different form of electro-healing, but a pointer nevertheless. Other disorders may originate from the pineal gland's possible inability to distinguish between artificial EM energy and natural light, thus upsetting the melatonin-serotonin secretion cycle.

Dr Nathan Rosenthal (also from NIMH) finds that by stimulating spring days during winter he alleviates SAD. He asks his patients to sit three feet from lights which mimic natural sunlight and are five times as bright as normal indoor illumination. After five hours a day for two or three days the patient's depression lifts, though continued treatment is necessary to maintain the alleviation.

In Britain there are two SAD clinics: at the Royal South Hampshire Hospital at Southampton, and at the Maudsley Hospital in south London. At the Maudsley's Institute of

Psychiatry Dr Stuart Checkley treats 50 patients a year who suffer from SAD. Having noted that most of the patients come from families with a history of depressive illness, and that four times as many women as men suffer from it, he has been applying a simple light box technique with good results. As a trial he also tried bathing a room in red from a harbour light. It had no beneficial effect; but when the same patients were put into simulated daylight conditions they recovered remarkably from their winter depression.

Acceptance of seasonal affective disorder as an illness is growing: there is now a British SAD Association run by Jennifer Eastwood, a former sufferer, while in New York Michael Terman of the New York State Psychiatric unit is a director of the light therapy unit there, with years of practical experience of the effects of SAD.

'It's a fascinating treatment in that the therapeutic modality is not chemical,' says Terman. 'I believe that in the near future their low cost will mean that light boxes will become environmental enhancing agents in the home.'

Experiments at the Jefferson Medical College in Philadelphia have shown that blue-green light is most effective at cutting melatonin levels, whereas violet and red light actually increases them slightly. Since the light from artificial bulbs is very red, melatonin levels therefore remain high under artificial light. This in turn stresses and depresses the organism's brain. (Curiously it has also been found that illuminating chickens for 16 hours each day improves their hen laying capacity, but there seems to be the corollary that their immune systems are impaired which in turn leads to a greater incursion of salmonella enteriditis. This monocellular creature and others like it such as listeria and legionella do not appear to be affected by electronic 'smog').

Though artificial light (around 100 lumens per square foot in the average office) may appear bright, it is by no means as bright as daylight – even an overcast sky outside will be ten times as bright. Thus artificial light intensity does nothing to improve melatonin levels.

A different technique, addressing the same basic hormonal mechanisms, has been developed by Audio Ltd of West London, though the objective here is actually to generate a relaxed state. Their therapeutic strobe flashes red light at the patient, reminiscent in some ways of gazing into flickering firelight, and after a few minutes it is said to promote relaxation and self-healing.

The first strobe light, made by Bryan Guyson and William Burroughs, was called the 'Dream Machine', and it was subsequently found that such photic drivers can induce hypnotic states – useful as an alternative to anaesthesia in dental surgery. C. Maxwell Cade, a pioneer of biofeedback, also used strobe lights as a relaxing agent, and for alleviating epilepsy and aiding arthritic patients. Dr Alex Forbes at Bristol's Cancer Self-Help Clinic uses a strobe to help patients get a good night's rest. All these devices are probably making use of the mechanism which stimulates melatonin.

There are, however, some contra-indications with strobe lights. Several patients lost consciousness under its influence – perhaps they became too relaxed, since no other effects were noted. In dance halls strobe lights are permitted only if the flash is not synchronized to the music. But fits can still occur – indeed are deliberately induced by some tribes – by a combination of repetitive dance music and the strobe-like sensations produced by whirling around.

Flashing lights are known to bring on migraine attacks, but paradoxically they may also be able to stop one in its tracks, and even prevent it from occurring. In 1986 Dr Duncan Anderson at Hammersmith Hospital's department of neurology found by chance, while investigating the patterns which people experience when looking at flashing lights through high-tech goggles, that they seemed to find the experience relaxing. So he tried it on someone with migraine and it halted the headache in minutes.

In a pilot-study of fifty migraine-sufferers wearing the goggles for ten to thirty minutes, 49 were substantially relieved and 75 per cent actually ceased to have migraines. The only side-effect was a tendency to doze off! The effects sound very similar to those achieved with the Silmaril lamp, but at a much lower cost. Production of the goggles is now under way by a firm called Migra Ltd of Hampstead, London, and Dr Anderson is embarking on a much larger study in order to try to understand how and why the goggle wearing works.

Apart from strobes, natural light can also induce epileptic conditions, as when someone drives past a row of evenly spaced trees through which sunlight is shining. Natural light has other special effects of its own: researchers at Cornell

University exposed 12 male and 29 female students to two independent light sources, one of which was closely matched to simulate natural day light (full spectrum light), while the other was an ordinary fluorescent tube of exactly the same 82 foot-candles illumination. After four hours exposure to each, significantly more students reported fatigue under the ordinary fluorescent tube.

Full spectrum lighting in offices is the gentlest form of electro-healing. The idea that artificial lighting which resembles daylight would be beneficial to health was pioneered in the mid-1960s by John Ott, who conducted a major research programme to evaluate the concept. A full spectrum bulb emits light at frequencies between infra-red (at 10^{12} Hertz) and high ultraviolet (at 10^{16} Hertz). The density of the various colours within the visible light range is balanced to match that found in natural sunlight.

In 1975 Richard Wurtman of Massachussetts Institute of Technology called for more research into full spectrum lighting, but the FDA is still somewhat sceptical, and in 1986 directed that claims for healing effects should not be made (they have the same view of negative ionizers). Nothing daunted, the developer of one full-spectrum lighting lamp, Oreste Bachechi of Albuquerque, New Mexico, believes that shining his light (Kivalight) onto food and water which are then ingested can indirectly produce healing effects.

As independent reporter, Tom Valentine from *Health Consciousness* magazine, confirms this after seven months personal trials in his own home. Improvements are said to include lessening of plaque round the teeth, growth and sturdiness in finger nails, and a general increase in energy. How some of these were measured is not stated, and no controls are mentioned.

Another manufacturer of full-spectrum lighting is Duro Test Corporation of New Jersey, a large US manufacturer of light sources. Their brand is called Truelite in America and Vitalite in the United Kingdom, where it is marketed by Anna Achilleos from Central London. Vitalite has been installed in a number of large firms' offices, such as Hewlett Packard, First National Security Bank, and General Motors Acceptances in the United States, Equity and Law and National Insurance and Guarantee Corporation in London. The staff of both organizations confirm they read better under the new-style lighting.

It is often said that full spectrum lighting tubes do not maintain their full spectrum during their entire life, and therefore might need replacement before they actually fail. But since lighting in offices only costs 1 per cent of total office costs, and three-quarters of that is the electricity consumed, changing lighting fittings twice as often would probably add only 0.25 per cent to costs, while gaining an important health advantage.

The Kivalight variant of full spectrum lighting has given rise to even more important claims by its manufacturers. They say that its effects assist in reducing arthritis, speed up bone fracture repair, drive away bacteria, and improve the taste of food and drink irradiated by it, even though the comestibles are left in their original packaging while irradiation takes place.

A Lancashire woman, Toni Roberts, is a tireless promoter of the Kiva effect, which she believes saved her life when anorexia, myalgic encephalomyelitis, vaginal problems, and severe allergies had almost driven her to suicide and she weighed only six stone. The Kivalight is also claimed to reduce stress from computer screen radiation. Such bold claims obviously need scientific verification by means of clinical blind trials, which might take years and a good deal of money to conduct. If the mechanism is also better understood acceptance may bring benefits in quicker healing to similarly afflicted patients.

Despite this renewed interest in light healing – or photo-therapy as it is becoming known – the healing effects of sunlight were already known to the Assyrians and Egyptians, who laid their patients in sand under the sun to heal. Later the Greeks took sun baths not only to alleviate diseases but also to improve athletic performance, and their famous physician Hippocrates pointed out that sunbathing could have a healing effect. Roman doctors copied the Greeks, introducing the solarium or sun-room into the homes of wealthy citizens as a supplement to their medical regimes, especially in the late Roman period.

A millennium after that the significance of the sun's light in the healing process was once again revived. In 1774 Faure treated patients with leg ulcers by the sun's rays, and only twenty years later Hufeland, a well-known physician, traced scrofula's cause back to a lack of light from the sun.

Modern   phototherapy   only   really   began   with   the development of radiation sources other than the sun, together with the means of measuring accurately their emitted frequencies and wavelengths. By 1894 Neils R. Finsen was treating tuberculous patients with ultraviolet light, based on the (false) assumption that it was the bacteriocidal properties – first identified by Downes and Blunt in 1877 – which induced the healing effect. He subsequently became the third ever Nobel Laureate for his pioneering work in treating psoriasis with UV B light, and in 1903 he introduced UV treatment for lupus vulgaris.

It was left first to J. Charcot to confirm that erythema (reddening of the skin) is produced by the ultraviolet component of sunlight, and following further research reports by the dermatologist P. G. Unna in 1885, Hamner was finally able to prove that sunburn was the result of overexposure to UV radiation. Even so, only in 1922 were the precise wavelengths and frequencies responsible for erythema determined (by Hauser and Wahle, and later by Henschke and Schulze). After that, Jesionek and W. Schultze found out that phototherapy assisted in the treatment of lupus vulgaris, and from the basic research of Winhaus and Pohl the formation of vitamin D from ergosterol confirmed the healing mechanism for these disorders.

About four out of five people will be cured within six weeks, usually by applying five treatments of fifteen minutes each week. To begin with each patient's erythema threshold must be ascertained in order to avoid over-dosing. Even so there are side effects, such as skin-wrinkling and the increased risk of carcinogenicity. The problems of squamous cell skin cancer after natural UV light exposure are serious, particularly in Australia, which has an incidence five times higher than Scandinavia, home of much research in this field.

In 1982 Valerie Beral and co-researchers from the London School of Hygiene and Tropical Medicine investigated the carcinogenic effects of the UV components of light from fluorescent tubes in offices. They found that there was a higher incidence of cancers in offices where the lighting was of this type, so UV treatment is not without risk. The components of UV light being administered must be carefully controlled: animal experiments seem to indicate not only that ultraviolet rays with a wavelength shorter than 320 nanometres are carcinogenic, but that treatment with high individual doses on skin not accustomed to it is particularly unfavourable. The Finnish are quite right to visit Madeira at Christmas rather than July!

Moreover, different parts of the body are of differing sensitivity to UV irradiation:

Back and Chest:	100%
Neck, extensor side of limbs:	70%
Face, scrotum, anal region:	50%
Palm of hand:	50%
Head with hair cut short:	20%

This in general reflects the customizing of certain parts of the body less habitually exposed. Comparing erythema produced by man-made radiation with that produced by sunlight, the latter has been found to have a shorter latent period and earlier maximum. There could also be a synergistic effect, when radiations from different parts of the EM spectrum are accumulated, e.g. from TV transmitters in hot climates. I was relieved to learn that Madeira has only one TV station!

A further example of sensitivity is given by the Norwegian university town of Tromsø, situated at 70° North, within the Arctic circle. Even though its inhabitants only see the sun between 21st January and 26th November each year, quite a few cases of psoriasis and photodermatosis are encountered there. When measurements were taken of the solar UVA and UVB radiation for each year between 1981 and 1984, it was found that early spring polymorphic light eruptions and the high daily ambient UVA between April and September, rather than UVB levels which are normally more harmful, were the cause. Since, however, there were only three clear days each month, any therapeutic effect of sunlight for treating psoriasis at that latitude would be poor.

Against this background it is important to realize that the amount of UV and other light reaching the earth from the sun can be influenced artificially by smog and dust particles to such an extent that UV rays of the shortest wavelengths are blocked out altogether, or conversely that damage to the ozone layer – whether caused chemically or electromagnetically – can let more UV light through than most organisms can handle. Sustained life is possible on the planet only in a narrow range of EM frequencies, because outside of these the co-valent H-bonds in our DNA are fractured. We live close below the threshold of tolerance, for that is also the frequency at which morphogenetic communication is optimal: ultraviolet radiation is immediately above visible light in the EM spectrum, and all organic cells seem to radiate tiny quantities of UV light, particularly when damaged, as Fritz Albert Popp has shown.

Bill McKibben, in his book *The End of Nature* puts this point more poetically and comprehensively:

Quite by accident, it turned out that the carbon dioxide and other gases we were producing in our pursuit of a better life – in pursuit of warm houses and eternal economic growth and agriculture so productive it would free most of us for other work – could alter the power of the sun, could increase its heat. And that increase could change the patterns of moisture and dryness, breed storms in new places, breed deserts. Those things may or may not have begun to happen, but it is too late to prevent them from happening. We have produced the carbon dioxide, we have ended nature.

We have not ended rainfall or sunlight. (In fact rainfall and sunlight may become more important forces in our lives.) Yes, the wind still blows – but longer from some other sphere, some inhuman place. It is too early to tell exactly how much harder the wind will blow, how much hotter the sun will shine . . .

The problem is not confined to human beings, in fact it is worse for the smallest creatures; zooplankton and phytoplankton, for example. As I write these words on Madeira it is Christmas and the sun is shining brightly on us sunbathers around the pool. But over on nearby Porto Santo, Elizabeth Leeson is collecting samples of plankton to count their density, a job she has done at Christmas for many years. This year the numbers will have fallen again. As McKibben says:

These creatures are sensitive to ultraviolet because they are so tiny: our skin can absorb most or all of the increased radiation, but it penetrates right to the heart of these organisms. There are indications that many plankton species have already reached their maximum tolerance for ultraviolet radiation.

Donat Haber of the University of Marburg in Germany told the *New York Times* in March 1988:

They are under maximum stress right now. Most of them are incredibly sensitive. When you expose a population of these organisms [to increased levels of radiation] they will die within a few hours. If they do not die they may sink lower in the water to avoid the increased ultraviolet, and this cuts
down the amount of sunlight they receive, reducing photosynthesis.

Without plankton many larger marine creatures, whales for example, cannot survive: about half the world's protein comes from marine species. The Madeirans, who used to fish, now grow bananas as out-of-season delicacies for the developed world.

St John was quite right about black light: incidentally, the word *marturo* in Greek not only means 'to bear witness', but also 'to bring warning'.

Like all other EM radiation, sunlight is subject to the laws of reflection, refraction, absorbtion, and polarization. So all areas of the earth where the surface is white – the Arctic and Antarctic for example – reflect light back upwards. It is precisely in these areas that the ozone layering is thinnest, suggesting that EM energy may be a co-factor in weakening the fragile bonds between the O_3 molecules which are ozone. Supporting evidence shows that the ozone layer is also slightly thinner above cities with high electromagnetic traffic, like New York, and even single power lines can have a detectable effect in the upper atmosphere.

Perhaps it is not only the chlorofluorocarbons, but also our new satellite uplinks and over the horizon radar systems which are perturbing the fragile ozone layer which protects us from mass extinction by irradiation. In presiding over the mass extinction of the whale and the marine mammals – many species of which are already falling prey to mysterious immune disorders – we may be heralding the end of nature as we know it.

Sunlight, therefore, is composed of a large 'cocktail' of electromagnetic energy at different frequencies and wavelengths, not all of which are beneficial, and it is important – particularly for those of us round the pool! – to be able to distinguish their effects. But this book is concerned principally with the healing effects of light, and its principal effect is on our skin.

Our skin is an incredible barrier, and is normally capable of excluding harmful radiations. Table 4.1 shows what sunlight's cocktail consists of:

Radiation Type	Wavelength (in nanometres)	Proportion reaching Earth (%)
UVC	200–280	0.0
UVB	280–315	0.04
UVA	315–400	4.9
Visible Light	380–760	39.0
Infrared A	760–1500	37.0
Infrared B	1500–3000	16.0
Infrared C	3000 plus	3.0
TOTAL:		99.94%

Table 4.1. The composition of sunlight

About 50 per cent of the sun's radiation is absorbed by clouds, and 20 per cent by contamination, though on mountain tops its intensity increases by 15 per cent with every 1000 metres, and also in the summer months, or during the hours around midday. It is the UVC radiation which perturbs oxygen in its ozone molecules. If the ozone layer did not prevent it, the UVC would convert the histidine found in the skin into histamine, which is a cell poison leading to sunburn. UVC is also bacteriocidal and might also disturb the bacterial colonization of our skin's surface, disturbing its fats, and causing consequent drying, fissures and flaky scaling.

The positive effects of UVC are that it helps form vitamin D from provitamins, and sometimes it is deliberately administered (from controlled artificial sources) to form histamine from histidine.

UVB radiation can also be dangerous, since it can damage the cells of the epidermis disordering their nuclei, and leading to erythema (reddening of the skin). The damaged cells are cast off as scales, but to protect itself against further damage the skin then forms a 'light callus', and permanent pigmentation or darkening. In March or November in the Northern hemisphere the body's sensitivity can be almost twice as great as in June, and its greatest sensitivity seems to be at 297 nanometres.

UVA radiation can also produce inflammation, but only at doses a thousand times stronger than UVB. UVA rays result in a number of health promoting and healing effects.

Infra-red radiation causes any body to heat up, and infra-red 'A' also accelerates the action of UV light generally, increasing circulation and including a cleansing and analgesic effect.

The chemical action of UV light is to mobilize organic phosphates and increase the deposition of calcium in the bones, thus helping bone fracture repair. In forming vitamin D it provides an anti-rachitic (anti-rickets) action and curbs disorders related to it such as spasmophilia (overexciteability in children). I once conducted some preliminary tests on the environments of hyperactive children, and found they were all sleeping in EM fields at power frequencies much above normal levels.

Other problems, such as softness of the bones caused by mineral deficiency (osteomalacia) and muscle spasms due to calcium deficiency (tetany) can be given prophylactic treatment with UVA. Also the respiratory lipid and protein metabolism can be improved. Rickets, psoriasis, and infant jaundice are not the only disorders which respond to UV treatment. There follow some of the others which this form of electrotherapy can alleviate.

Eczema
Both the seborrheic and particularly the follicular form respond well to UV radiation, and with children UV therapy is preferable even to other local therapeutic methods if carefully administered.

Herpes Simplex
The recurring forms of herpes, which, as is well known, can frequently be produced by intense sunlight (herpes solaris), can be treated with good results even to the point of preventing relapses.

Ichthyosis
This is so called because the patient presents with a body covered in fish-like scales, a very unpleasant condition indeed.

A combination of ointments, Vitamin A, and UV doses below the erythema threshold are effective, presumably because of their direct influence on keratinization.

Lichen ruber planus (Pruritis)

The subsiding of pruritus through UV light treatment is an impressive sight. UV treatment is often continued after the inflammation has subsided to prevent recurrence.

Urticaria

This is so called from the latin word for stinging nettles, and shows as a mottled red rash. Though results are variable if the cause itself is not eliminated, a course of UV treatment helps to normalize the skin.

Other rarer conditions, such as mycosis fungoides, alopecia areata, dermatitis herpetiformis, vitiligo, pemphigus vulgaris, and pityriasis can benefit from UV treatment.

As if this catalogue of UV healing effects, all of which have been proved clinically, were not enough, UV light has also been shown to lower blood pressure, because the blood forms additional red blood cells (erythrocytes) leading to an improvement in oxygen transport. Thus UV light can be used to treat secondary anaemia and helps to avoid heart attacks (myocardial infarction). Finally, bilirubin – the product of the disintegration of the red blood pigment which shows up as childhood jaundice – can be broken down by UV light if excesses of it are formed in new-born infants.

Sunlight also seems to have a generally beneficial effect on the autonomic nervous system, and its UV light component leads to increased resistance to viral and other infections by increasing complements in the blood. On the other hand, when the sun cycle is at its height the radiation is too much and damage to the immune system seems to bring on epidemics of influenza.

The bio-effects of UVB in treating psoriasis clearly need closer examination: is UVB treatment of psoriasis safe? In 1982 Olle Lark and Gunnar Swanbeck from the Dermatology department of Gothenburg University, Sweden, undertook a study to answer this very question. In Sweden, sunlight is the dominant cause of skin cancer, and the main aim of their research was to find out whether or not extensively UVB-treated patients ran a greater risk of developing skin cancer than did controls.

In Gothenburg, which has a latitude of 58° north, the inhabitants get relatively low UVB radiation from the sun. Fortunately, at Gothenburg UVB treatment had been carried out for psoriasis for several decades, and the researchers had access to accurate treatment records going back 20 years. (During this period carbon arc lamps had predominantly been used, which, in view of Valerie Beral's findings of an association between fluorescent tube lighting and increased cancer incidence may have introduced a somewhat confounding factor into the results.) However, some 85 cases, who had each received over 100 UVB treatments, and a control group of 338 persons were identified, matched for sex, age, and geographic region.

The prevalence of persons who had premalignant or malignant skin lesions, at the time of the tests or in the past, was 5.9 per cent in the psoriasis cases, against 10.1 per cent in the control group. This difference is not statistically significant, and the researchers concluded that it is unlikely that the psoriasis patients treated in the past have any prevalence of skin cancer above the norm. Furthermore, though a correlation was found between pre-malignant and malignant skin changes and advanced age and outdoor occupation, no such correlation was found for factors such as sex, skin type, or travel to southern latitudes. The Scandinavians round the pool would be quite relieved to know that!

The technology of UV irradiation is complex, but has advanced prodigiously during this century, especially during the last few decades, and the more harmful effects have been eliminated. Sunbeds are much safer these days!

Some of the products developed from phototherapy are exotic, and none more so than the Silmaril lamp. This lamp consists of two halogen car headlamps in front of which is imposed a fast-spinning disc in which have been set precious stones such as rubies. The equipment is shined on the patient for about twenty minutes. It is claimed to reduce migraine, M.E. and other disorders. Though the machine was originally developed in Bristol, it was promoted actively by Dr Anne Wooley Hart prior to her death in 1990. Not many models were sold, in view of the cost, and despite large private capital investment.

Another commercially developed product is Biotone, from Fetouris of London, which delivers monochromatic light through the visible spectrum and a little beyond. This instrument is claimed to be 'a natural method of healing through bio-stimulation of the cells by light. This results in a higher cellular activity, increased tissue repair, increased blood circulation, and muscle relaxation.' The claims are probably valid, to judge from what we already know about the effect of visible light, but the difference is that very pure light frequencies are produced by the instrument.

This naturally leads to the whole concept of colour therapy, which goes somewhat further than full spectrum lighting. Its proponents claim that different colours have specific healing effects. One of the pioneers of colour therapy in Britain is Theo Gimbel. He has been organizing residential weekend courses at his Hygeia Studios at Tetbury, Gloucestershire, for some years.

We all know that certain colours can be restful to the eye, while others can be energizing. Applying and refining this basic concept lies behind colour therapy, and leads to some bizarre examples. For instance, the Yorkshire police, copying an American idea, have painted prison cell walls designed for violent prisoners bright pink, and have found that after twenty minutes in such cells the inmates are very much calmer.

5. The Alternative Therapies

Until there is some real understanding of the part the vital body plays as the broadcaster and as the recipient of feelings, thoughts, and ideas, there will be little progress made in the right understanding of modes of communication.

Alice A. Bailey, *Telepathy*, 1950.

This century has seen the rise of many curious new therapies – if they can be called so – which claim to cure organic disorders by means other than pharmaceutical or chemical. Such techniques often work – but then so does the art of the witchdoctor on occasion. If statistically the chance of a patient's recovery from some malady is 50 per cent – and of course it may be 100 per cent, such as in the case of a mild cold – then any new applied therapy has only to achieve chance levels of success, and it will have 'cured' half the patients. The therapist may then delude him or herself into quoting successes, and fail to think about the other half who failed to recover.

This makes it very difficult for outsiders to confirm the real benefits of any therapy. The brain is continually healing the body naturally, anyway, through its control of cell division (mitosis): the body replaces some 500 million cells each night, mostly during paradoxical sleep. I have already offered an explanation of paradoxical sleep, suggesting that the brain's radiations are what in fact control the cell cycles phases, and other vital instructions for cell repair and organization. Interference with that mechanism from radiating EM fields may be why neoplastic events, errors of DNA transcription, and immune deficits arise. It should also be possible actually to assist the brain's radiations both by amplifying them and also by curbing outside interference. Both objectives are what might be called subtle, since the frequencies and intensities of fields thus applied are extremely small. Many doctors are not unaware of this: by advising you simply to take 'bedrest' they are really saying 'Let your brain do the healing and do not disturb its action.'

This chapter examines the various ways in which 'alternative' or complementary medicine might work even better than simply letting the brain to get on with the healing process, and examines it from an electromagnetic viewpoint. Others use phrases such as subtle energies or energy medicine, which probably frighten off the ordinary scientist because they are so imprecise. But I hope that it will be possible to explain all these techniques in terms of ordinary physics in a way which hard science can begin to accept.

Homoeopathy

This therapy relies on administering minute amounts of substances that in a healthy person would produce symptoms like those of the disease; it is claimed to be effective in disorders as diverse as allergies, influenza, carbuncles, and diabetes. It is claimed to be 'absolutely effective in cases where there are no pathological tissue changes'.

As usual, lack of a proven mechanism has been responsible for incredulity on the part of conventional medicine. No more glaring example of this can be found than the investigation by John Maddox, a former editor of *Nature*, James Randi, a professional conjurer, and Walter Stuart, a rather shadowy figure alleged to have been connected with American intelligence, into certain experiments claiming to provide evidence of biological effects from water which had been diluted beyond the Avogadro number.

The Avogadro number is named after an Italian scientist who in 1811 deduced the principle that equal volumes of all gases at the same temperature and pressure contain the same number of molecules. He didn't actually calculate the number: fifty years afterwards a German, Goschmidt, did it, measuring the exact number of molecules per mole (the molecular weight in grammes) and this turned out to be 6.022×10^{23}. A simpler way of saying this is that if you dilute a preparation 24 times, each time by a factor of ten (or 12 times by a factor of 100) there should be none of the original molecules left in the dilution.

So to claim specific biological effects from a potion diluted beyond the Avogadro number flies in the face of conventional physics and chemistry. But this is just what the experiment carried out in 1988 by Dr Jacques Benveniste at a French laboratory, Inserm 200, claimed to demonstrate.

What Benveniste actually did was to dilute antibodies called immunoglobulin E (IgE) way beyond the Avogadro number and then see if the dilute could still cause basophils (a type of white blood cell) to degranulate. This white blood cell, when exposed to the actual antibodies, always reacts by degranulating, in other words, discharging the granules inside it and thereby releasing histamine.

Since degranulation can be detected by staining, it would be a fairly easy matter to detect the extent of any degranulation empirically in a dilute which had once contained the antibodies. Not only did the tests appear to demonstrate this (by over 20 per cent), but also showed regular peaks and troughs of the effect at specific levels of dilution (see figure 5.1).

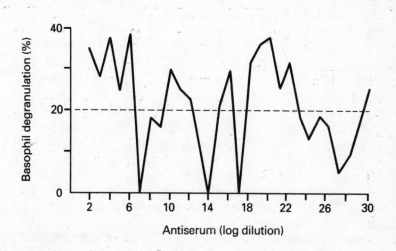

Figure 5.1: Benveniste's diluted basophil experiment

The tests were repeated elsewhere in several other independent laboratories, with the same positive results. Naturally Benveniste was anxious (as were his funding sponsors, a homoeopathic firm) to get the results published in a respectable journal, of which *Nature* is one, but the editor hung back for two years, and only agreed to publish if he could actually witness a replication of the study.

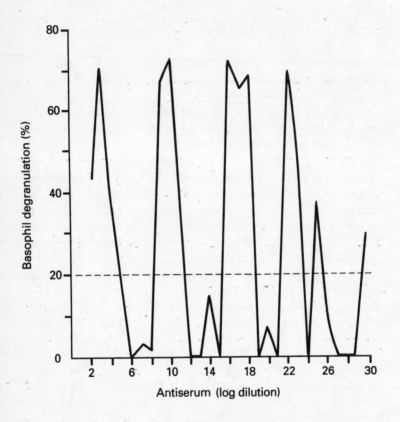

Figure 5.2: The fourth demonstration experiment with unexpectedly high peaks

Thus it was that the three sceptical investigators visited Benveniste's laboratory in July 1988 to watch the tests being replicated. For the first three days of testing they seemed to work: the first three tests repeated routinely the results already reported. In the fourth test new factors were introduced which caused unexpectedly high peaks (see figure 5.2). But the last three tests all proved negative and did not confirm Benveniste's claims.

What new factors might have upset these delicate experiments? Well, we know that electromagnetic fields can inhibit the cytotoxicity of lymphocytes. Benveniste, not being familiar with biomagnetics literature, was probably unaware of the impact such fields can have, but I think this is exactly what happened. To quote *Nature:* 'On the third day a new dilution series was single-coded in front of a video camera.' I do not know which camera was used, but a model popular at that time (Videostar) gives off a power frequency electric field of 35 Volts per metre at three inches in front of its lens (where one might close-up a shot of a test tube) and this field does not drop to the normal room field strength (8V/m) until two feet out from the camera. I measured this recently with the appropriate instruments.

The magnetic field measured 70 nanoTesla at three inches from the lens, and it took the distance of a metre before the needle on my instrument dropped to the normal background level (13 nT in this case). Benveniste did not suspect the effect of these intrusive fields on the water in his patterned test-tubes. Dr Boyd in the 1920s, on the other hand, realized that he had to screen such fields out by means of copper sheeting, when he was convincing a similar investigating team (from the Royal Society of Medicine on that occasion) that homoeopathic potions could be distinguished from other solutions by a human subject.

The next new factor which was introduced at Benveniste's laboratory was that an aluminium foil was taped to the ceiling, ostensibly to hide the coded test-tubes' identity. This puzzled Benveniste at the time, because everybody knew the codes anyway. Since all EM fields can be focused, reflected, and refracted just like light, this scintillating foil may also have had an effect on the diluted water, because apparently the video camera was continually played upon it, not to mention the electric lights in the room themselves.

Finally, 'the squad left with 1500 photocopies'. When these were made and how near the copier was to the experiment room is not stated, but since photocopiers emit large quantities of ozone, a very unstable form of oxygen, it is probable that this too had a devastating effect on the tubes as a result of the huge ion flows thus generated.

So, the first three open and blind tests worked, controls being impeccable, whereas on the last three days, when a number of different electromagnetic influences were introduced into the environment, the results were at first exaggerated and finally ruined.

The question is, if such a test does indeed provide evidence of bio-effects, what might be the mechanism? Several physicists have been looking at this problem, among them Cyril Smith of Salford University's Electrical Engineering Dept, and Emilio del Giudice from Milan. In the 1960s researchers suggested that the process of dilution (potentization as it is called) induces electrochemical changes into the dilute. Cyril Smith, a bespectacled academic with a certain regard for facts, however bizarre they might appear and quite prone to bring out dowsing rods to prove a point, suggested that water has a helical structure capable of remembering frequencies to which it has been exposed.

When measuring the effect of electrical frequencies on allergy patients he found that increasing the frequency produced a rhythmic pattern of stimulation and inhibition similar to homoeopathic preparations. A German researcher, Ludwig, gives the principal frequency for arnica 1000X as 9.725 kHz. Cyril Smith discovered an interchangeability between dilutes potentized with homoeopathic preparations and water in a sealed test tube which had been exposed to alternating magnetic fields at one of the patient's neutralizing frequencies. The magnetically charged water would act as an allergy-neutralizing dilution.

He was actually anteceded by that same Dr Boyd who discovered in the 1920s that a sealed phial of homoeopathic solution in a 10M potency introduced into his 'Emanometer' – an instrument based on Albert Abrams' Oscilloclast – could be repeatedly distinguished from a neutral solution, with odds of thirty million to one of this happening by chance.

The incredulity of Sir Thomas Horder of the RSM in those days was almost painful to behold:

On resuming in the afternoon, it was decided to attempt first a series of trials under the most rigorous test conditions obtainable. Two fresh test bottles were therefore selected by the investigators and filled with equal quantities of active and neutral drugs as before. No corks were used. At the suggestion of Mr Dingwall, additional screens were arranged above the shelf on which the bottles were shuffled in order to preclude any possibility of observation from above, and while the test was in progress Mr Whateley Smith visited the upper rooms with the same object in view. Dr Boyd was absent throughout the preparation of the specimens and the conduct of the test.

The operator was right in eleven cases out of eleven. (The twelfth case was not carried out because the operator reported contamination). 'The chance of accidental success,' calculated Horder, 'was 1 in 2048.'

Further testing produced a success rate with a chance of accidental success of 1 in 33,554,432, reported Sir Thomas. Faced with this overwhelming evidence that something was definitely happening, he nevertheless concluded:

This communication is preliminary only. It is clear that the work must be continued and that the nature, the significance, and the practical application of the facts here brought to light must be studied fully . . . The ways in which Dr Boyd tracked down and eliminated such sources of 'contamination' as seemed to arise from time to time was particularly convincing, as also was the fact that Sir Thomas Horder and Dr Heald, when acting as subjects, could definitely feel an alteration in their abdominal muscles as specimens were inserted or withdrawn through the hatch without their knowledge.

The investigating team concluded:

Certain substances, when placed in proper relation to the Emanometer of Dr Boyd, produce, beyond reasonable doubt, changes in the abdominal wall of 'the subject' of a kind which may be detected by percussion. This is tantamount to the statement that the fundamental proposition underlying in common the original and certain forms of apparatus devised for the purpose of eliciting the so-called Electronic reactions of Abrams, is established to a very high degree of probability.

Even so, the team's final conclusion probably put back medical scientific progress by half a century, and condemned

radionics practitioners thereafter to work under cover and in
fear of their reputations:

It is impossible to emphasize too strongly that nothing in this
communication is to be taken as implying that . . . any
justification – physical, pathological, nosological or clinical –
exists for the direct use of either the Abrams or Boyd apparatus
in diagnosis or treatment.
  To sum up. The conclusions arrived at in this communication
leave the position of the practising electronist as scientifically
unsound and as ethically unjustified as it was before. They give
no sanction for the use of E.R.A. in the diagnosis or in the
treatment of disease. Nor does there appear to be any other
sanction for this kind of practise at the present time.

Pity. Maddox and his team made a different but equally
damning conclusion fifty two years later: '"High dilution"
experiments a delusion', went the editorial in Nature, 'The
phenomenon as described is not reproducible in the ordinary
meaning of that word.'
  Boyd was dealing with an environment which was at the time
relatively free of man-made electromagnetic radiation. But
even then, in 1924, when radio programmes were just
beginning to be transmitted, Boyd was careful to screen his test
room against unwanted RF radiation by cladding it in a copper
sheeting:

The laboratory measures about 12 feet by 8 feet and is
completely screened throughout as a precaution against radiation
from sources other than the specimen under test; the floor is
made of copper sheets, while the walls and door are covered
with thirty mesh copper gauze, all such surfaces being in
metallic contact. Gauze screens are disposed about the room in
various positions in such a way as to reduce the chances of
interference by reflection to a minimum. In the end wall remote
from the door is a window in which copper gauze takes the
place of glass and which is provided with a hatch about 12
inches wide by 18 inches high, fitted with a sliding gauze panel
which can be raised or lowered by means of a chain and pulleys.

If Benveniste had insisted on the same conditions – and he
was working in our modern-day intensely electromagnetic

environment – then the three investigators from *Nature* would have come back with a quite different story.

Water is usually defined as H_2O, though it almost invariably contains other trace elements and minerals, as the label on any mineral water bottle confirms. The simplest atomic composition is one oxygen atom bonded (loosely) to two hydrogen atoms. Oxygen has six electrons in its outermost shell, each of these travelling in pairs and in equilibrium. Since the outermost shell of an atom seems to want only a minimum of eight electrons, the oxygen atom is happy to accept the idea of sharing two more, one from each of the hydrogen atoms. The trouble is, both of these electrons are negatively charged, which is a naturally 'repulsive' situation, in that the electrons don't really want to stay near each other. This kind of bond is called 'co-valent' – as opposed to ionic, where one atom gives away its electrons to the other.

Water is therefore very unstable, in that the slightest electrical charges arriving in it can disturb its H-bonds, changing their patterns of connection. Humans are mostly made of water, so one might say that we too are very unstable! In terms of memory, this instability is a very useful asset: water can act just like the electromagnetically charged chromium dioxide recording tape. One recording can thus be easily wiped out by another, or even simply by bringing a magnetic field near to the tape. This is why Benveniste's experiments were ruined by the video camera's fields.

But that is only part of the problem. How can these specific patterns of water, so small in themselves, ever begin to cure organic disorders? One can start to answer this by realizing that since we human beings are mostly made of water, anything we ingest will have a patterning effect, because all materials are slightly magnetic, even foods. When ill, the homoeopath will argue, we are suffering from improper patterning, which is ultimately having a structural effect. The dilute, however, changes that pattern.

These remedies have been discovered simply by trial and error, based on a few preliminary precepts. The first is the principle of 'like will be cured by like' (*similia similibus curentur* in Latin). This rather mysterious concept really means that if your symptoms are similar to those induced by eating a certain substance, then that substance will also, in the right dilution, eradicate the symptom.

Dr Samuel Hahnemann, the father of homoeopathy, probably never thought of the idea in terms of electromagnetic energy, but to translate what appears to be a completely barmy idea into basic electronics I shall invoke the *heterodyne principle* – familiar to electronics engineers. This means simply that if an undulating wave is causing a disturbance in the atmosphere (or on the sea, or in free space), one can eliminate it by creating another wave whose peaks and troughs are the exact reverse of the first wave. The mechanism works with sound waves too: in effect it just means shifting the wave's phase by 180 degrees. Albert Abrams is said to have illustrated the phenomenon in his lectures by showing that the waveform of malaria can be neutralized by the waveform of quinine. Heterodyne comes from a Greek word meaning 'the other wave'. The final question must be, if we allow the argument so far, well, what is causing the disorder in the first place?

Paul Solomon, an exponent of the mystery school philosophies such as the old Pythagoreans practised, tries to answer that question by suggesting that the normal electromagnetic field of any human being acts as a shield against external radiations, whether they be infections, thoughts, or even other people. Unless we retain our spiritual self-reliance he says, we diminish that shield and open ourselves to foreign insult. I do not expect any hard scientist to accept that view, but electronic smogging works on almost the same principles – in modern warfare at any rate.

Any injury to the body will set up 'injury currents' which have associated electromagnetic fields. This would begin to explain healing itself in EM terms. Any noxious substance, if enough of it is eaten, would do the same since its electrochemical action during digestion will also cause electromagnetic fields of a very specific signature. The same goes for any organic (i.e. bacterial or viral) invasion of the body. As Lakhovsky said, all disease is simply a war of radiations.

Homoeopathy works by suppressing those radiations so that the brain can issue organic cell repair instructions without interference from the water or other components of our body which have been wrongly patterned.

Cyril Smith of Salford University has proposed a helical structure for water – like DNA – which is capable of 'remembering' the pattern of EM fields which have entered it. The helical shape, he argues, might have the required electrical properties for storing frequencies. 'The structure waves would occupy those EM and acoustic modes of propagation appropriate to a helix.'

Dilution on its own does not necessarily provide an effective remedy: only by shaking the dilute vigorously are the H-bonds re-established to give the new structure. George Vithoulkas, in his book *Homoeopathy, Medicine of the New Man*, also explains it in terms of electromagnetism:

Electromagnetic fields are characterized by the phenomenon of vibration. As electrons race around atomic nuclei, they first move in one direction and then another, as viewed by an external observer. This oscillation back and forth occurs at a specific frequency which is determined by the type of sub-atomic particle and its level of energy. For our purposes, however, the significant point is that everything exists in a state of vibration, and every electromagnetic field is characterized by vibration rates (or frequencies) which can be measured.

The human organism is no exception. To grossly over-simplify a highly complex situation, one can visualize an individual human being as existing at a particular vibrational frequency which may change dynamically every second, depending upon the mental state of the person, internal or external stresses, illness, and so on. The electromagnetic field is very likely the 'vital force' which Hahnemann referred to.

Once a morbific stimulus has affected the electromagnetic field of a person, things may progress in two ways. If the person's constitutional state is quite strong and the harmful stimulus quite weak, the electromagnetic field changes vibration rate only slightly and only for a short time. The individual is not aware that anything has happened at all.

If however, the stimulus is powerful enough to overwhelm the vital force, the electromagnetic field undergoes a greater change in vibration rate, and effects are eventually felt by the individual. A defence mechanism is called into action which may involve changes on mental, emotional or physical levels.

The defence mechanism of an organism is called into play only when a stimulus is truly a threat to the existence or well-being of the organism. It is only then that the organism sets in motion processes which are felt in the patient as symptoms. The symptoms of a disease are nothing but reactions trying to rid the organism of harmful influences which are merely the material manifestations of earlier disturbances on a dynamic electromagnetic level.

Vithoulkas goes on to explain how a homoeopathic remedy is chosen to match the disease. But it occurs to me, and this has been verified by Dr Cyril Smith working with another doctor, Jean Munro, that electromagnetic fields can be substituted for the remedies, and presumably can be determined exactly by seeing what is the electromagnetic signature of the disease. Once that is known, a phase shift of 180 degrees will neutralize it, and the only task remaining is to make sure that the field strengths are the same. Believe it or not, that is precisely what radionics practitioners have been doing for decades.

Radionics

The connection between radionics and homoeopathy has now been drawn. Radionics is the art (or is it a science?) of diagnosing and curing at a distance. One of its earliest pioneers after Abrams and Boyd was Ruth Drown, who suggested in the 1930s that we all live connected in one vast field of energy. Well, we do, if you regard the earth's geomagnetic field in that way, since without it our body clocks start to go awry. But she went further, proposing that diagnosis and healing could be carried out at a distance using very small samples of the patient's body cells.

This theory alone would have brought her into disrepute, but she went even further, inventing a camera which she claimed could take pictures of people thousands of miles away. Today of course we do this all the time by means of TV, transmitting the pictures around the world via satellite uplinks. But in those days the idea sounded more like some Victorian spiritualist seance or Sunday afternoon parlour game. Drown's pictures do look quite realistic. Inevitably though, no orthodox scientist believed her story, and she was discredited as a quack, to her dying shame. Without the equipment of television available to her, it is still incredible if she was indeed able to do what she claimed.

David Tansley gives a good account of radionics in his book of that name, and traces its history to today. Yet his chapter on how radionics works is woefully lacking, and covers only three sides, most of which are confined to expressing the concept of how our universe is one interconnected whole. There's nothing wrong with this statement, and any quantum physicist would agree with it: the movement of one single electron from the outer shell of one single atom in any place in the universe will be 'noticed' in that the electromagnetic charges of all the others everywhere will have been modified by this quantum change.

But that doesn't go very far towards explaining radionics, or even the transmission of wireless communication in general, of which radionics is simply a sub-set. What is lacking is the additional component, which I call cerebral morphogenetic radiation (CMR), which is a way of saying that the brain's control of the cells of its body is carried out at a distance by electromagnetic means, and any other signals will interfere with or enhance its electromagnetically conveyed instructions.

Energy Medicine

The entire mechanisms of vibrational or energy medicine as it is now called, were explored in 1988 by Richard Gerber, a physician. Its concepts are in fact quite easy to understand. Albert Einstein proposed the following famous equation:

$$E = mc^2.K$$

We all know the formula, but how many of us understand it? It really is quite simple: E stands for energy, m stands for mass (or material), c stands for light, and K is a constant. So a common way of explaining the formula is to say that all energy is simply matter multiplied by the speed of light squared, times a constant.

Turning the same formula on its head leads to:

$$m = E/c^2.K$$

This makes the amazing statement that all matter is simply energy divided by the speed of light squared, and if this is true then we are all nothing but dancing packets of energy, expressed in terms of electromagnetic fields. We are nothing but lumps of energy! And if that is true, then every time I move my arm I am simply moving energy through the air about me. My seemingly solid arm isn't solid at all.

Gerber suggests that human organisms are 'a series of interacting multidimensional subtle energy systems', and if these systems become unbalanced there may be resulting pathological symptoms which manifest on the physical/ emotional/spiritual and mental planes. Like the radionics practitioners, he describes how these imbalances can be healed by rebalancing the subtle energy templates with the right frequency of vibrational medicine.

Interestingly, says Gerber in his introduction, many of the healing modalities discussed in this book are often less expensive and considerably less toxic or risky than conventional medical or surgical methods, since the physical body is actually a complex network of interwoven energy fields. Attempting simply to alter one part of it will have energetic repercussions on the rest. The real key, however, to treating such recurring conditions of disease may not be the 'quick fix' physical solutions, but in the realm of repatterning the organizing energy fields which direct the cellular expression of dysfunction.

Any holographic film contains the interference pattern of the whole photographed object – and even a small piece of it will display the entire object when a reference beam is shone upon it. The DNA macromolecule is also a reference containing all the information necessary to recreate that particular organism.

Even so, points out Gerber, our knowledge of DNA has been inadequate thus far to explain how differentiating cells in the human foetus find their way to the appropriate spatial locations where they will carry out their specialized functions. So his concepts stop where my notion of cerebral morphogenetic radiation and Sheldrake's morphic resonance begin.

The Bach Flower Remedies

There are many natural substances which vibrate at frequencies which assist the healing processes. Flowers, for example, have many different colours and hues, which really means we see their different frequencies along the EM spectrum. The specific curative possibilities of these unique frequencies which emanate from certain flowers was recognized in the 1930s by Edward Bach, who began his career as a bacteriologist. He noticed that certain gastrointestinal bacteria seemed to be related to specific illnesses like arthritis and rheumatism. If these bacteria, he surmised, aggravated the illnesses, then perhaps boosting the immune system would diminish them. Diluted vaccines prepared specifically against these pathogens did, he found, exactly that: they improved the seemingly unrelated arthritic and rheumatoid patient's condition.

From these conceptual beginnings Bach was surprised to learn the similarity of the technique he had stumbled upon with the homoeopathic principle of like cures like, and went on to classify seven bacterial groups whose pathogenic effects could be mitigated by seven vaccines – or Nosodes as he called them. Progressing further, he found that the different patient groups were also temperamentally similar. Eventually, he ignored the disease type altogether and applied the Nosodes purely according to the patient's emotional temperament, which worked even better. In doing so, he predated the only-now emerging science of psychoneuroimmunology by half a century.

Bach's final profound insight was that if the patient's specific emotional state could be brought back into equilibrium, then the disease-type associated with it might also be mitigated:

Fear, by its depressing effect on our mentality, causes
disharmony in our physical and magnetic bodies, and paves the
way for (bacterial) invasion. The real cause of disease lies in our
own personality.

This precept obviously was the thinking of a sensitive man. He used his sensitivity to nature to identify 38 flowers and natural products which could be used to reharmonize perturbed emotional states. He died at the youngish age of 56, but his Flower Remedies have remained in use for over 50 years since then, prescribed by naturopaths all over Europe and America.

Flower Essences

His work was continued and extended in America by the Flower Essences Society, founded in 1979 by Richard Katz. If by now you hope for a really scientific approach to these things, you will be disappointed: the source of his new knowledge were none other than psychic readings by a so-called 'channel', collected into a subtle energy medical textbook by Gurudas, a researcher from Boulder, Colorado.

But such concepts badly need explanation in terms of the hard physical and biological sciences. Part of the problem may be that as a result of the specialization of science the realms of the two are as distant as separate galaxies. Fortunately, the growing science of bioelectromagnetism seems to be rejoining the two.

Scientists have been finding that some crystalline substances are liquid, for example, rather than the hard, diamond-like stones with which we are familiar. Impressively, none other than Gurudas makes a telling point in our gradual understanding of their role in bio-communication:

There are various quartz-like crystalline structures in the physical and subtle bodies that augment the impact of vibrational remedies. In the physical body these include cell salts, fatty tissue, lymphs, red and white cells, and the pineal gland. These crystalline structures are a complete system in the body, but not yet properly isolated and understood by modern medicine. Crystalline structures work on sympathetic resonancy . . . [Could this be a reference to the crystalline structure of DNA?]

In similar fashion, vibrations of radio-wave frequency strike a crystal in a radio. The crystal resonates with the high frequency in such a way as to absorb it, passing along the audio frequencies which are perceivable by the body.

What he seems to be saying is very close to the idea of morphogenetic radiation, but without the vital component of the brain. Some of Gurudas' insights were extraordinary:

The actual [plant] essence, of course, is the electromagnetic pattern of the plant form. Even as here there are nutritional elements found in various plant forms that ye partake of for the physical body, so in turn are there various parameters of biomagnetic energies discharged by flowers and various plant forms.

No wonder microwave-cooked food tastes different! After all, if microwave energy can cause sickness even at miniscule power densities, why should not plant essences be able to 'cause' health?

Aromatherapy

One of the more-thumbed books in my bookshelf is a work – it's more of an adventure really – by Valerie Ann Worwood called *Aromantics*. She has been practising a therapy called aromatherapy for more than twenty years. The title gives it away but my favourite quote from the book is:

When you touch the force is with you . . . Although this force is tangible, it remains for a future Nobel prize-winner to explain what exactly it is. Photographs of human energy fields have been taken by researchers at Duke's University in America, Dr C. Guja of the Institut V. Babe in Bucharest, Rumania, and students of Dr Kirlian all over the world, amongst others, but there is no certainty that the energy fields they are picking up are one and the same. Indeed it is more than likely that there are several invisible energy patterns yet to be explained.

Invisibility, as such, should present no barrier to accepting the real – we do after all, turn on our transistor radios and portable TVs and expect to receive a variety of programmes on a variety of wavelengths. And it is clearly ludicrous to demand 'scientific proof' as a prerequisite to belief when science is itself in the on-going process of disproving itself and changing its own rules, while at the same time extending the 'facts' at its disposal by identifying and explaining what already exists. The 'discovery' of DNA occurred millions of years after DNA first started doing its thing.

Worwood's blend of aromatherapy and massage relies on the topical application (by human hand) of specific aromatic oils called quintessential oils. They are called quintessential because the essences were originally reduced five times. This concentration gives them extraordinary penetrative power: not only do they smell distinctive – and our speed of reaction to smell is said to be faster than to pain or noise – but their presence can be detected in the urine only four hours after being applied to the skin.

These oils are very complex compounds: they contain terpenes, alcohols, esters, aldehydes, ketones, phenols, and more, so that their chemical complexity baffles scientists. And though they are virtually all – like homoeopathic remedies – drawn from natural substances like jasmine, geranium, or cedarwood, it is also true that about a third of modern drugs are based on them. Their healing properties include bactericidal, anti-viral, anti-toxic, anti-neuralgic, diuretic, antirheumatic, antispasmodic, anti-venomous, anti-inflammatory, granulating stimulating, deodorizing, and circulation stimulating. They are used to treat cancerous wounds, gangrene, skin diseases, burns, bronchitis, and glandular imbalances, among other things.

Worwood describes well the antiquity of essential oils:

Millenia before people needed 'scientific proof' of a thing before they would believe in it, the quintessential oils were being extracted for medicinal purposes. Indeed, the aromatic plants of the world are humanity's oldest and dearest friends. When every one was dropping like ninepins during London's Great Plague in 1665, the only group of people not affected were those working in the perfume houses which, in those days of course, used only the natural quintessential oils. And the spice wars of history weren't just about gourmands adding spice to their food or perfume to their powdered wigs, but about people trying to get hold of the raw materials which would prevent them drying.

The ancient Egyptians burned a different aromatic substance at different times of the day, with a special 16-ingredient mixture called kyphi at sunset, in thanks to the sun god Re. When the tomb of Tutankhamen was opened in 1922, pots and vases were discovered, some containing unguents – like spikenard and frankincense – which must have been placed there over three millennia ago. Finally, in Exodus 30 we find:

Moreover the Lord spake unto Moses, saying take thou also unto thee principal spices . . . and thou shalt make it an oil of holy anointment, an ointment compound after the art of the apothecary: it shall be an holy anointing oil.

Given their chemical nature, why should one attempt to explain the mechanisms of aromatherapy in electromagnetic terms? Worwood has no difficulty in doing so:

It has long been known that nature's quintessential oils modify the body's electromagnetic fields, and as we discover more about the body's electrical patterns this becomes an especially interesting aspect of them. According to the latest research, the body is a composite picture of electrical patterns, with each organ and area having its own unique pattern which becomes disturbed when the body is ill. Some of the most interesting research yet to be carried out on quintessential oils must surely be in this area.

The founder of modern aromatherapy was René Maurice Gattefossé, who published his first book in 1928. His discovery of the remarkable healing properties of essential oils is described by practitioner Robert Tisserand:

René Maurice Gattefossé was a chemist, and at first his interest and his research was confined to cosmetic uses of essences. Two things happened which helped to extend his interest. Firstly, cosmetics often contain antiseptics: Gattefossé had soon gathered enough information to convince him that many essential oils had even greater antiseptic properties than some of the antiseptic chemicals in use at that time. Secondly, one of Gattefossé's hands was badly burned when a small explosion occurred in his laboratory during an experiment. He instantly immersed it in neat lavender oil, and was only partly surprised when he found that the burn healed at a phenomenal rate, with no sign of infection, and leaving no scar.

One of Gattefossé's basic tenets was that natural substances should be used in their entirety, and that individual components of the oils were not as effective as the whole. If one were to provide an electronic analogy, it might be that in listening to fine music one should not cut off the frequencies above say 20,000 Hz because that takes the edge off the quality of the sound.

Tisserand's classic book on the *Art of Aromatherapy* scarcely reaches its fiftieth page before he turns to its connection with the life force:

If we recognize the existence of this life-force, and that it is the only power which can produce health within us, we will realize that we must work with and not against it. We cannot heal directly; we can only help the body to heal itself by encouraging the natural healing force within, and allowing it to do what it wants to do. So often we interpret sickness as something

unfortunate and undesirable, and yet often, especially in acute
disease, it is a manifestation of the body's attempt to restore
health and harmony.

He then discusses the positive and negative aspects of the life
force, ch'i's, yin and yang, and describes how many of the
essential oils contain one or other of these forces, so that by
applying the converse to the body its equilibrium is re-
established.

It is likely that massage assists this process by adding the
electromagnetic field of the masseur to the mechanisms at
work. The principal effect, however, is the subtle alteration of
the body's pH value – the atomic equivalent of yin and yang.
Lucien Roujon, in his book *L'energie Microvibratoire et la Vie*
points out that the blood of a young person in perfect health
has a pH value of 7.0 to 7.2, which is almost exactly half way
between acid and alkali, and just slightly alkaline. Each cubic
millimetre of such blood contains about 60 milliards of
hydrogen+ ions. This figure can reach 600 milliards of ions
to reach a pH value of 6 (acid) or 6 milliards of ions (alkaline),
both extremes being associated with grave illnesses:
poliomyelitis gives a pH value of 6 and cancers a pH value of
8 or more.

Simply by adding the correct number of ions, one can bring
the blood condition back into equilibrium, and this can be
done either by direct electromagnetic field exposure, by
homoeopathy, or by aromatherapy, since they all change the
character of the body's own fields. Thus in modern terms all
these therapies are restoring ion balance to a cellular
imbalance, whether you describe it as yin and yang, tuning the
chakras, acupuncture, or any of the subtle energy medicines.

They are all using nuclear electromagnetic energy to make
the correction. This is because the pH or hydrogen potential,
though considered in terms of its chemistry – its degree of
acidity or alkalinity – is in fact a magnetic factor. We help
plants return to health by altering the pH factor in their soil.
Some plants prefer acid, and others alkaline soils. It is not
surprising therefore that individual plants have individual pH
characteristics can be applied to balance the pH value of
organisms which ingest them, or to which they are applied
topically. Aromatherapy, it seems, has a fundamentally
electromagnetic origin.

Electroacupuncture

Robert Becker, apart from his pioneering work on organic regeneration and wound and bone repair, also conducted an investigation into acupuncture. This therapy was developed in China from 500 BC onwards and it is still practised there today mainly for anaesthetic and analgesic purposes.

The philosophy of acupuncture strangely is also based on polarity: the negative in this case being called 'yin' and the positive 'yang'. Health depends on maintaining equilibrium between these two, so that 'ch'i', a non-material energy, can flow or circulate unimpeded throughout the body via fourteen channels called meridians, which have nothing to do with the nervous pathways known to the physiologist.

Should any imbalance arise it manifests itself as an obstruction or resistance to the passage of ch'i, and this in turn presents as illness. All these concepts will make the electronic engineer feel at home: they are exactly how electronic circuits work, with their passage sometimes deliberately held up by resistors, stored by capacitors, and woe betide any circuit where the wire has come adrift!

The acupuncturist, like the electronics engineer, first evaluates the symptoms presented by the patient. Then he or she manipulates the relevant acupuncture point (a place where the meridian arrives at the skin's surface) by means of a fine silver or gold wire inserted into the body, sometimes surprisingly deeply. This original technique has now been modernized by the development of electroacupuncture: here, instead of a needle, an electrode is applied on or near to the skin's surface at the same place as the needle would have been inserted.

Fine: but this basic description of acupuncture and its new offspring lacks one ingredient: what is its basic mechanism? It was this question which aroused Becker's interest. In trying to find answers, Becker first measured the electrical characteristics of the acupuncture points. Did they really exist? If so it might be that their physical presence could be detected by some electrical difference. Sure enough he found that half the points were of much lower electrical resistance than their surrounding tissue, and also that AC impedance was different. Resistance between acupuncture points was also lower than between control points off the acupuncture 'circuit'. Apart from implicating natural endorphins as the possible mechanism whereby acupuncture achieves its analgesic effect, Becker was unable to offer any further explanation of these findings.

His reason for the idea that endorphins were involved was based on the discovery that after low frequency electro-acupuncture the resulting analgesia could be turned off again or blocked by an intravenous injection of a substance called naloxone (an opiate antagonist). Cyril Smith, who has also devoted many decades of research to electromagnetic bio-effects at Salford University, also found that endogenous endorphins in the brain could be induced by electromagnetic fields.

Electroacupuncture, or merely applying a conductive metal filament from outside the body, will clearly set up local oscillating circuits and change the electrical potential of the acupuncture point – it will most probably lower it if gold or silver, which are highly conductive metals, are used. Thus there is a direct comparison between removing electrical resistance from a circuit.

The puzzle is, why should the body need a conducting circuit which does not travel along the conventional nervous pathways? No one at present knows the answer, but I have a feeling that it must be to do with electromagnetic conduction, rather than electrochemical reaction. One suggestion is that the acupuncture points are an entrance point for negative ions. Negative ions are certainly absorbed into the body through the skin. For example, A. L. Tchijewsky, a Soviet scientist whose pioneering work on ions dates back to the 1920s, but who was unknown to the West until recently, argues convincingly, according to Fred Soyka, that the nerve endings under the skin act as receptors for ions and have a direct influence on the body and its organs. Dr Walter Stark, the Swiss physical chemist and biophysicist, believes that the point where the ions most readily enter are the acupuncture points. On this basis the needles of traditional acupuncture presumably act as conducting channels, and it is interesting that conventional acupuncture techniques leave the needles in place for some time so that this can happen.

Tchijewsky and his co-worker Lapitsky carried out numerous experiments with ions: in one of these they tried raising small animals in de-ionized air, and within two weeks all of them died. In other studies animals deprived of oxygen and on the point of suffocation were quickly revived by neg-ions alone.

Touch Therapy

Another complementary therapy connected with electromagnetism is variously known as touch therapy, the laying on of hands in Christian churches, touch for health, and even massage. Its history as a therapeutic technique is very ancient: even as far back as 1552 BC the concept is mentioned in the Egyptian Ebers papyrus. The Greeks used it for healing the sick: Aristophanes mentions the use of laying on of hands for healing in Athens (perhaps tongue in cheek), whereby sight was restored to the blind, and fertility to the barren.

In medieval Europe the royal touch was said to cure scrofula (tuberculosis). More recently, in 1943, following accidental exposure to extremely powerful electromagnetic fields, certain naval ratings apparently were prone to dissolve into thin air – to change from material into energy, thereby becoming invisible at light frequencies. The change was often initiated by magnetic or metallic objects, according to one eye-witness. This incredible metamorphosis, a reputed side-effect of a trial known as the Philadelphia experiment, which terrified the patients who were susceptible to it, was also said to be prevented through the laying on of hands by any nearby bystanders.

The effectiveness of touch as a healing mechanism may also be connected with the natural electromagnetic energy found in every organic creature, and its capability of balancing and stabilizing the body currents of a fellow species. In one interesting experiment designed to see whether faith or psychic healing had any substance, Dr Donald Krieger, Professor of Nursing at New York University, chose haemoglobin as a biochemical indicator of healing energy in human beings. Krieger found that a group of patients subjected to healing treatments had a significant increase in haemoglobin values compared with the controls.

Mothers whose babies are born prematurely are often separated from them when the infants are put into the incubators and surrounded by electromagnetic monitoring instruments. Survival rates of such pre-term infants are often poor. But allowing the mother to handle and stay near her neonatal child has been found to be a useful therapeutic technique, and poses the question whether a mother's electromagnetic field is beneficial to the neonate in some mysterious way.

Distant healing was practised by Edgar Cayce with apparent success over many miles. In a way it is more puzzling to wonder why medical science has done nothing about research into these directions, than to ponder over the mechanisms themselves. If they are indeed electromagnetic in nature, then we shall have to revise our views fundamentally on topics as diverse as the speed and mechanisms of evolution (the Sheldrake hypothesis is that good new genetic ideas are transmitted at a distance between members of a species, thus introducing beneficial mutations much faster than Darwinism would predict), and even revise our derision for the ancient crafts of witchery.

6. The Ion Lady

Fire and air do not dissolve masses of earth, because their
particles are smaller than the interstices in the earth's texture, so
they have plenty of room to pass through without exerting force
and leave it unbroken and undissolved.

Plato of Athens, Timaeus, c. 350 BC

During her long years as head of the British government
Margaret Thatcher acquired an enviable reputation for
fortitude, determination and single mindedness; the Soviets
called her the Iron Lady. What sustains a leader during those
times when anyone else might have succumbed to pressure?

On Saturday 20th May 1989, one of Britain's popular
newspapers, *The Daily Mail*, provided part of the answer: in
a word, electro-healing. John Hamshire, a *Mail* reporter, traced
some of the Premier's early morning or late night
appointments to an obscure semi-detached house in
Boscombe Road, Shepherd's Bush, West London. Though its
exterior gives nothing away, 'it's like Taj Mahal inside' he
reported.

What might be taking place behind those innocent doors?
Secret discussions with foreign heads of State? British
intelligence briefings? No. Mrs Thatcher was simply taking a
bath. It was a bath with a difference, though, for at Veronica
Zubadri Smith's private clinic Mrs Thatcher was being sauna-
ed, massaged, and then immersed in a bathtub of water
through which a weak electric current was passing.

'According to a neighbour', wrote John Hamshire, 'Madame
Veronique's clientele include the Princess of Wales and Terry
Wogan (presumably not in the same bath).' Ayurvedic

treatment, apparently, is the application of aromatic massage, supplemented in this case by the introduction of negative ions via the bath. 'It's a very lucrative business', said Madame Veronique's ex-husband Sir Frank Smith, 'but it seems to do the trick.' At a reputed £700 per session one might hope so.

What are ordinary folk like you and me, and ordinary scientists too, to make of all that? More to the point, why can't we all share in the P.M.'s secret treatment on the National Health? I could, as a matter of fact, probably accomplish the same ion effect for anyone at a fraction of the price. For Veronica Zubadri Smith was doing was simply administering negative ions to the human body.

When this news broke, the P.M. was in a dilemma – on the one hand she was (rightly) making use of electro-healing. But on the other there were powerful vested interests – the military, the pharmaceuticals corporations, the telecommunications industry, the power transmission and distribution authorities – all of whom would not wish to admit that bio-effects, either good or bad, existed apart from the undeniable heating of organic tissues or electrocution.

I am constantly surprised, in these days of mass consumerism, when the United Kingdom market penetration of most major domestic electric appliances is well over 50 per cent, that the penetration of negative ionizers is still less than 10 per cent of British households. The answer must be, I suppose, that there is not only a good deal of ignorance about their benefits, but that their only visible effect seems to be to make the places near them dirty.

The dozen or so United Kingdom manufacturers of neg-ion machines continually struggle to persuade their customers to buy: their products are easily available in health shops and even in large chain stores, though their prices are said by some to be much higher than the manufacturing costs warrant. Annual United Kingdom sales of neg-ion machines in 1988 were 400,000, against 50,000 in 1982, but this compares with some 16 million British households, so annual uptake is only 2.5 per cent. This is going to change, though probably not for the reasons it should. As one report put it, 'Even if proven health benefits are discounted and just their cleaning ability considered, neg-ion machines have a sales potential far greater than at present.'

Take the vacuum cleaner, for example, where market

penetration is high. It cannot be denied that vacuum cleaners do a good job in collecting dust. The problem is, they work by sucking air from the carpet through a porous bag. The bag has to be porous, otherwise air cannot pass through it. So any particles of dust smaller than the tiny holes in the bag will also escape, shot skywards from the carpet into the air we breathe. These particles are potentially as dangerous as asbestos or formaldehyde should they lodge in the lungs. They include pollens, lead derivatives, bacteria and viruses – all of which escape the vacuum cleaner's trawl. Since we breathe about 1,700 litres of air each day we actually do our own microparticle vacuum cleaning, expectorating the result or solidifying it as nasal mucus. Each inhalation in a city contains about 70,000 pollution particles, not all of which ever leave the body. Not figures to sniff at.

What most neg-ion manufacturers have missed is that these particles should not be let loose again to soil the area round the ionizer or even recirculate, but should be captured permanently for subsequent disposal. Most multi-stage ionizers remove only the larger pollutants, leaving smaller particles to be deposited by electrostatic precipitation back onto walls and furnishings, and bacteria too would have simply been recycled if not destroyed by the 7 kV electrostatic charge within the machine. The better ionizers can remove up to 95 per cent of particles, down to 0.01 of a micron, but many viruses are smaller than this (down to 0.005 of a micron) so are left in the air.

The other useful function performed by a neg-ion generator concerns the negative ions themselves. Our modern environment has created a large variety of chemicals – synthetic fabrics, plastics like formaldehyde and so on – which simply were not there a century ago. In modern homes it also generates an imbalance of static charges through our use of TV, radio and many other domestic electric appliances.

So, dust particles can easily become positively or negatively charged when some of their constituent electrons are shaken free and attach themselves to other molecules. Normally most atoms are in electrical balance, with the protons of the atom being positively charged and their electrons negatively charged. So when an electron has been vibrated free from an atom or molecule that molecule is left with a net positive charge. The electron will then roam free until it happens upon another atom to which it attaches, thus causing the atom to have a net negative charge.

In a rural location one might find at least 1,000 neg-ions per cubic centimetre, in a city there might be only 300 per cubic cm, and in an office as little as 50 neg-ions per cubic cm. Why are neg-ions beneficial to health? the mechanisms are not fully understood, but they do seem to assist oxygen transport by the blood. The blood absorbs oxygen from the lungs, carrying it round the bloodstream delivering it to the muscles in a complicated process which vitally depends on electrical charges.

The negatively-charged ions assist the process, but positively-charged ones appear to hinder it. Moreover the interior structure of nucleated cells is also kept in place by microtubular filaments – like scaffolding poles – and these filaments are also polarized, growing from the positive end towards the cell wall. Their polarity is disturbed by positive ions (like forces repel), leading to intracellular structural weakness.

There are many other examples in nature of how positive ions slow down the healing process – post-operative bleeding for example is greater at the time when the full moon's influence increases the ratio of positive ions at the earth's surface. Before a thunderstorm or when winds blow from dry places the air contains more pos-ions and people tend to get irritable and aggressive, whereas near waterfalls, mountains, and the sea negative ions are more prevalent, hence such places are attractive for health and recreation (literally). (Madeira, with its wonderful waterfalls, mountains and Atlantic seas crashing against the rocks, has an abundance of all three.)

The normal ratio of negative to positive ions is 15 to 85, because positive ions are repelled by the earth's surface which is slightly positively charged. This ratio is changed by environmental conditions, and by the fact that ions tend to congregate on the ends of pointed objects like pyramids, standing stones, buildings, or mountain tops. It is probably just as important to breathe in negative ions as it is to avoid diesel fumes, and one report from Surrey University's Department of Occupational Health confirms improvements in alertness following the surreptitious introduction of neg-ion machines.

These investigations into the effects of neg-ions on

performance were carried out in the early 1980s by Dr
Hawkins of Surrey University's Department of Human Biolog
and Health. He measured just how much the influence of both
positive and negative ions on various tasks, such as mirror
drawing, visual and auditory reaction time, rotary pursuit, and
bead threading. All of these activities were improved
significantly by the introduction of neg-ions (except bead-
threading where a non-significant improvement was seen),
whereas pos-ions made no difference. Temperature was also
important: performance showed a measurable improvement at
19°C, less effect at 22°C, and by 29°C there was no measurable
effect at all. Humidity also had an influence, low humidity
(30%RH) assisting a greater beneficial effect from air ions than
high humidity (70%RH). This might have been caused by ions
clustering around water vapour molecules as they do around
dust particles, making them unavailable to the individual.

Hawkins also studied the effect of ions on people working
in a computer suite. In the study, 50 males and 4 females were
monitored in the room, which had been fitted with two neg-ion
generators which developed 3,500 neg-ions per cubic cm.
There were measured only 100 positive ions in that volume.
When the machines were not operating the average neg-ion
count fell to about 550 while pos-ions rose to 500 per cubic
cm. Though there were VDUs in use, most of the personnel
were computer operators. Nevertheless neg-ion levels near the
VDUs were probably reduced because of the high positive
charge on the screen.

In the study design the workers had no idea if the machines
were on or off. The results were gained by means of a
questionnaire completed at the end of each work period, and
were therefore subjective. But it was very clear that headaches
and nausea were drastically reduced as a result of the neg-ions
generated by the machines.

Another interesting result was that the neg-ions were
particularly effective at night (the workers operated a three-
shift 24 hour programme). It is quite remarkable that despite
these and other indications of the beneficial effects of neg-ions
in commercial offices I have not yet found any major
newspaper or broadcasting station where neg-ion machines
have been installed in such vital areas as direct screen editing
or in sound studios.

Coupling an ionizer with an aromatic oil or fragrance

...he same effects as the former Premier's ...e concept of the galvanic bath, like Ayurvedic ...s by no means new: it was first introduced in ...te Spa by a Dr Fernie, who patented the ...sion was made of metal and had a pole fitted ...n the patient grasped. The technique was abandoned in 1906, however, amid claims that it could be dangerous. Today Dr Peter Fischer offers similar bio-electric treatment at the Alternative Health retreat. In Mrs Thatcher's home there is a negative ionizer, and its healthful effects have been confirmed by her husband, according to the *Mail* article.

Another beneficial effect of neg-ions is to reduce the serotonin level, a change which appears to benefit migraine sufferers. The melatonin-serotonin cycle seems particularly affected by electromagnetic fields. Studies by Krueger and Kotaka in 1969 first suggested that negative air ions might cause a reduction in levels of brain serotonin. Serotonin and melatonin are two hormones which are only secreted by the pineal gland and none other. The result of exposure to light is to increase serotonin levels. High serotonin in turn makes one hyperactive and ultimately exhausted, a discovery which Krueger and his co-worker in 1960, Richard Smith, had already made.

They also found that the pos-ions were responsible for this effect, whereas neg-ions seemed to have an *anxiolytic* effect, that is they are calming. A recent (1990) study by C. J. Beardwood and P. M. Jordi of Cape Town University's department of physics found that neg-ions also inhibit the action of morphine. They measured this in a curious way by watching how often rats flicked their tails in response to thermal stimulation: the rats which had been injected with morphine then neg-ions decreased the latency of their tail flick, suggesting it had inhibited the action of the previously injected morphine.

In another study by Bary Wilson in 1986, the exposure of rats to AC electric fields caused a marked suppression of the normal nocturnal increase in pineal melatonin. So it appears that neg-ions could assist in creating the conditions necessary for protein synthesis (most of which occurs at night), whereas pos-ions, by stimulating serotonin production and ensuring hyperactivity, have a preventative effect, since the alternating circadian rhythms regulated by the serotonin-melatonin cycle under pineal control are disturbed.

If my notion of cerebral morphogenetic radiation is right, the melatonin might be acting as a damper, minimizing electrical activity in the body, so that the brain's own signals enjoy a better signal-to-noise ratio. Migraine sufferers may well get their malady as a result of the brain trying to send out its signals against an undampened background. By reducing serotonin levels the background 'noise' is reduced and the migraine alleviated.

Among the scientists most interested in studying the impact of light on the pineal gland are Russel Reiter from the University of Texas and A. J. Lewy of Oregon Health Sciences University's department of psychiatry. Rieter has found a variety of neuroendocrine dysfunctions as a result of exposing rats to ELF at night and thereby altering nocturnal melatonin production. These include changes in reproductive physiology, alteration in circadian rhythms, and perhaps effects on the immune system and tumour growth.

A. J. Lewy had also discovered that bright light suppresses melatonin production in humans, so, without changing the activity-rest cycle, he shone very bright light early in the morning on patients whose circadian rhythms had shifted and who had become depressed as a result. The result was to re-set the circadian rhythm correctly and alleviate the seasonal affective disorder (or SAD as it is known).

David Blask from Tucson's University of Arizona (where presumably they get a lot of sunlight) has also been studying the effects of the pineal gland's melatonin secretions on cancer formation. These have been implicated in the growth of neoplastic tumours like breast cancer, melanoma, sarcoma, leukaemia, and pituitary prolactinoma. It seems that melatonin injected in the later afternoon can inhibit the growth of carcinogen-induced breast cancers, though there are several guesses as to how that happens. Blask thinks that melatonin may inhibit the action of the mitogenic effects of oestrogen. My own view is that the melanin lets the brain's own signals get through and these are tumour inhibiting in themselves.

How does a negative ionizer work? Individual models differ, but the general principle is that air is drawn into the machine by a fan, and then passes over positively charged elements. These plates attract the negatively-charged molecules and repel the positively-charged. The treated air then passes through an alternatively pos- and neg- charged plates which collect the dust particles and finally the air then passes over negatively-charged plates which capture the positively charged ions, letting the neg-ions out into the surrounding room.

A typical ionizer must emit an electric potential difference of 4.5 kiloVolts in order to split an oxygen molecule (O_2), and a maximum of 8.5 kV, since to exceed this produces ozone (O_3) which is dangerous in quantities larger than 0.04 parts per million. Thus the better neg-ion machines emit towards 7.0kV, have a separate washable collector plate or replaceable filters, and are sturdy enough to resist breakage and consequent risk of shock.

Among the disorders said to be benefited or alleviated by ionizers are hay fever, asthma, migraine and headaches, arthritis and rheumatism (possibly), tension, emphysema, catarrh, sinusitis, and bronchitis. Ionizers are also important in VDU operating rooms. This is because the VDU emits positive ions from the screen surface – you can test its static charge and see a build-up of dust on the screen, which may then be inhaled by the operator, or cause 'dry eye' and skin irritations or eruptions. The charged particles also inevitably get caught up in the ADP-ATP cycle and are delivered to the muscles, most often the hands or upper limbs which are most in use and nearest the machine.

In consequence the actin and myosin microtubular filaments which are responsible for muscular contraction (they are similar to the intracellular filaments) lose charge and induce a syndrome previously known as RSI (repetitive strain injury) but now called upper limb disorder after it was realized that there was no correlation between its incidence and the number of key depressions performed by sufferers.

A recent study by Kaimanovich and Krupitska (*Journal of Bioelectricity*, 8, 1989) from Leningrad Shipbuilding Institute calculated that electronic fields and ionic gradients were the important factors in orienting microtubules within cells along the field direction. Since VDUs give off such fields this suggests the mechanism whereby prolonged exposure to VDU radiation may well incapacitate the microtubules and hence induce a sensation of muscle fatigue. Ionizers, by reducing the ionic gradients, could help to alleviate such effects.

Though there are over 5 million or so VDUs in use in Britain alone today, the annual sales of ionizers have not risen in line, principally because office administrators are not aware of the connection between positive ion emission and RSI. Also because most current models seem to cover adjacent areas with fine particulate dust.

One concern about ionizers is that, being mains-powered and on all the time, they create – like any other electric appliance – continuous power frequency electromagnetic fields. Therefore installing an ionizer by your bed may have contra-indications. One manufacturer, Mountain Breeze – a firm associated with Maharishi Mahesh Yogi's Transcendental Movement – has overcome this problem by encasing the ionizer, properly insulated, in a metallic Faraday cage. Its Air System 7000 model also filters the air in three separate stages: the collector, then an electrified resin wool, and finally an activated carbon deodorizer.

In comparing different models of ionizer there are several important criteria: (a) physiological range, measured in metres from the apparatus; (b) the smallness and percentage of particles captured (in microns); (c) the air cleaning volume per hour; and (d) the high voltage charge induced. Some dosimetrists also refer to the ion density at one metre, (this is about 750,000 ions per cc. for most models) but such data is very variable even in one machine, since temperature, humidity, and ambient air flow, amongst other things, can easily distort the measurements from one hour to the next.

The power consumption of an average ionizer is very low at about 40 watts. Retail prices can vary from less than £20 to more than £300, depending on the capacity and finish. New developments in ionizers include those specially designed for cars. One couple I know find that their young children, who used to become fractious and hyperactive when taken on long car journeys as the static built up, are now much more docile after installation of the car ionizer. Another recent development is the cordless re-chargeable ionizer, which can be taken into, for example, stuffy hotel bedrooms.

While there is still a great deal of improvement to be made in ionizer technology, the days when such machines were actually dangerous are long past. There is also a new attitude at the Federal Drug Administration in the United States (which has not before allowed claims that such machines are beneficial to health), as the mechanism of their biological effects are becoming better understood.

A 1988 report by the London Ionizer Centre (LIC), owned by Jonas Cleary of Clear-Air, lists fourteen different makes of ionizer, most of which are made in Britain. In the United States they are only allowed to be sold as air cleaning devices, but in the United Kingdom their sales literature freely extols the electro-healing properties.

The LIC report assessed many of the models from the viewpoint of construction and value for money. Its general conclusions at the time were that most ionizers were too expensive in relation to production cost, but that if certain technological difficulties were overcome a large market awaited the ionizer manufacturer. Table 6.1 lists some of the smaller domestic machines.

Name	Power of Charge (kV)	Retail price (1988 £stg)
Medion	n.a.	85–59
Triple Air	6.5	49–95
Salton/Superionizer	9.0 to 15.0	49–84*
Mountain Breeze	6.5	44–95
Ionflow	n.a.	42–50
Freshenaire (Amcor)	8.5	39–95*
Cruisair	4.6	39–95
Pulsair	4.6	39–95
Astrid	n.a.	39–95
Oasis	6.5	39–95
Ion Drive	7.5	35–65
Sun Domus	7.5	29–95
Daneng	7.25	28–00*
Clean Air	7.0	22–99

* incorporates transformer, rather than solid state devices.

Table 6.1: Ionizers

The larger machines, such as Mountain Breeze's Air System 7000, the Biotech 2001 (a Canadian machine) and the Ionostatic, can clean between 140 and 600 cubic metres an hour and are suitable for offices. These can cost several hundred pounds, and often incorporate fragrance dispensers and natural wood finishes. With some the filters must be replaced, while others are designed so that the collector box can be renewed, washed and replaced (when thoroughly dry).

One dramatic demonstration shows how quickly a neg-ion machine can clear a large smoke-filled plastic dome: they certainly do work very effectively as room air cleaners! Some of the ionizers use transformers to convert energy from 240 volts to the higher kiloVoltages needed to ionize. Others, which are arguably more advanced, make use of solid state technology by incorporating a series of diodes and capacitors, which are probably safer, and the circuitry is in any case very simple.

I have described some of the possible biological mechanisms which cause neg-ions to be so beneficial. Indeed, the negatively charged ion seems a common denominator in some complementary therapies: magnetotherapy, where the north pole field (negative) is applied to the skin; acupuncture, where the acupuncture points are said to be specially capable of absorbing negative ions, and have a field gradient round them for this purpose; even aromatherapy, where the pH value of a natural substance is used to regulate the body's equilibrium.

As the picture of how organisms in general (and human beings in particular) maintain their cellular health becomes clearer, the role of ions assumes greater prominence. Since any movement of ions in effect is the same as an electric current, and such currents inevitably create electromagnetic fields around them, we are beginning to uncover a mechanism of life and coherent inter-cellular communication.

The cells in our bodies join together to form tissues, which in turn form organs. But the means of cell-to-cell connection is by various kinds of junction. Of these, one variety is the tight junction which forms an impermeable barrier for example between two organs such as the brain and the bloodstream. Another is the gap junction. This is the commonest type of cell junction, and allows small water-soluble molecules to pass directly from the cytoplasm (interior fluid) of one cell to another. You might have thought that the communication between two cells was chemical, but far from it! It was demonstrated in 1958 (by inserting microelectrodes into each of two interacting nerve cells in the nerve cord of a crayfish) that a voltage gradient applied to the electrodes set up a current flow between the two cells. It means that inorganic ions (which carry current in living tissues) could pass freely and directly from one cell to another.

This may prove to be a useful mechanism for transmitting information down nerve fibres. These gap junctions, however, are also found in nearly all eukaryotic cells, so what could be their function in those places? As Alberts, Bray *et al.* say in their lucid textbook of molecular biology (1983),

The real difficulty lies in understanding why gap junctions occur in tissues that are not electrically active . . . It is possible that the coupling of cells (in embryos) might provide a pathway for cell signalling over longer distances . . . In principle the resultant sharing of small metabolites and ions provides a mechanism for co-ordinating the activities and responses of individual cells in such tissues.

What an important insight! Altering the cellular environment – whether it be by modifying intracellular pH, increasing concentrations of Ca^{++}, or simply exposing the cell to ions or external electromagnetic fields – rapidly (within seconds) affects the permeability of the gap junction, hence the cell's ability to communicate with its neighbour.

The plasma membrane (which immediately surrounds the cell wall) is like a sandwich with its outer layer positively charged and its inner layer negatively charged. The potential difference between the two is only about one tenth of a Volt, but since the membrane is only 5 millionths of a metre thick, this suggests a voltage potential difference of 20,000 Volts per metre, a formidable electrical barrier, were it not for the existence of the gap junctions. The arrival of negative ions on the membrane surface may diminish that potential difference, making intercellular communications easier, whereas pos-ions will make it more difficult.

We simply do not know for sure how external electromagnetic fields affect cellular communication. Some scientists are beginning to suggest that ion cyclotron resonance is at the root of electromagnetic bio-effects. Ion cyclotron resonance sounds frighteningly technical, but as usual, the concept can be fairly easily explained.

Mark Wilson was only 14 when he won a young scientist of the year award for a neat experiment in ion cyclotron resonance which showed that in certain conditions magnetic fields can impair the short-term memory of rats in mazes. He explained:

My hypothesis was that short-term memory loss may be due to the brain calcium ions (Ca^{++}) being affected by these types of EM fields. Changes in brain calcium motion, caused by magnetic and electric fields that meet ion cyclotron resonance conditions could affect short-term memory.

First he had to set up his equipment so that ion cyclotron conditions were occurring. He constructed an eight-armed maze with a central arena. The rats had to remember down which arm of the maze to travel from this arena to obtain a food pellet. Above the central arena was an electromagnetic exposure system which would resonate the calcium ions. Just as an opera singer has to hit precisely the right note in order to resonate and thus shatter a wine glass some distance away, so young Mark had to calculate the right conditions to generate the precise resonant frequency which would resonate the calcium ions in the rats' brains. (A similar machine using sound frequencies – the infrasound machine – was capable of resonating whole buildings at a distance in a similar way.)

The magnetic fields involved of course included the earth's own geomagnetic field. By tuning his instruments Mark added the vertical component of another AC field of 0.27 gauss, because the already established formula for finding ion cyclotron resonance demanded a total of 0.77 gauss (if the mains electricity frequency is 60 Hz as it is in America).

Then he borrowed a field meter and by measurement found that the electric field strength was 48 Volts per metre in the central arena – a strength often found in domestic residences, but nevertheless much higher (by about four times) the normal strength of 8–12 Volts per metre. In other words it is not unlikely that we are creating ion cyclotron conditions in our own homes near some items of electrical equipment.

Normally the calcium ions would move through the gap

junction. But if a free ion moves into a constant magnetic field it accelerates so that its path bends into a circle. The frequency at which the ion circulates depends on its mass and charge, and the strength of the field. Add a second magnetic field that oscillates at the same frequency and the particle accelerates further (particle physicists exploit this effect in their cyclotron accelerators). That is how the phenomenon comes to be called ion cyclotron resonance.

There are a few problems with this idea. First, the calculated radius of the cyclotron orbit is as wide as one metre for a resonating calcium ion, and it is almost certainly going to collide with some other particle in the cell before getting very far. Also, inside the cell the calcium ion is surrounded by a tight shell of water molecules which will affect its resonant frequency anyway. (Homoeopaths please note!)

In 1990 Valeri Lednev from the Soviet Institute of Biological Physics at Puschino hit on a solution to this dilemma at almost exactly the same time as John Male did so at the British National Power's research establishment at Leatherhead. It is quite extraordinary how often in science the same new ideas occur at the same time to scientists working in very different parts of the world and completely unaware of each other's research. (It is, I suspect, yet another example of cerebral morphogenetic radiation, but I dare not argue the point!)

Lednev proposed that a weak oscillating magnetic field could loosen the bonds which occur between metal ions like calcium and some proteins in the body vital for metabolism. If a bound calcium ion is placed in both static and oscillating fields it will continually oscillate around its equilibrium position in its binding site. Applying a steady magnetic field will cause it to rotate (or precess) about the direction of the magnetic field at a frequency which is exactly half the frequency of the bound ion.

Adding an alternating magnetic field at the cyclotron frequency disturbs the precession sufficiently to loosen the bond between the ion and the protein, even though the frequency is far below the level normally accepted as ionizing. The implications for electro-healing are large: 'It could lead to new therapeutic applications of magnetic fields' commented the *New Scientist* in August 1990. 'For example, many diseases can be attributed to too little or too much calcium in the body. Applying magnetic fields could provide a simple non-intrusive way of modifying the calcium levels.'

Lednev did actually try to verify his hypothesis, using a muscle protein called myosin. He found that it phosphorylated (added a phosphate) several times more easily in the presence of a steady magnetic field combined with an alternating magnetic field. The reason why the myosin did this was that it depends on the binding of calcium in calmodulin to control phosphorylation, and somehow the calcium had unbound in the presence of these fields.

This sounds all very theoretical and unimportant. But now think about what happens to a VDU operator in front of a computer screen. Many such operators get pains in their hands and upper limbs, and no one has been able either to explain it or cure it. But all our muscles depend vitally on myosin to contract them. After manual effort the myosin microfilaments need to recharge their polarity. But if they phosphorylate, it feels as if the effort has been made, even though no work has been done. And this could be the result of magnetic field exposure from the VDU and consequential ion cyclotron resonance. This is why VDU operators often feel muscle pain only usually felt after overexertion.

That's not all. Alzheimer's disease has been linked with an excess of aluminium in the brain. Passing a magnetic field through the brain at the right cyclotron resonance frequency might well be able to detach the aluminium ions and re-establish a normal personality to the confused patient. I have come across one case where an Alzheimer patient completely regained his lucidity for a while after a brain scan. It is beginning to look as if tampering with intercellular ion flows could be beneficial to health, once we know what we are doing.

Conventionally we make a clear distinction between ionizing and non-ionizing radiation: and nobody denies that ionizing radiation damages cells. But physics is really a science of statistics and large numbers, and is therefore only approximate. As Schrodinger says: 'Only in the co-operation of an enormously large number of atoms do statistical laws begin to operate and control the behaviour of these assembles, with an accuracy increasing as the number of atoms increases.'

In biology, however, we are dealing with very few atoms and their electromagnetic relationships: a single photon of light is perceivable by the human eye. The DNA coding structure is dependent on just a few very specific hydrogen bonds, and if they fracture entirely new meanings may be imputed to the genetic message. It is conceivable that the term non-ionizing in reality is also a statistical term, meaning that only a relatively small number of ions are being created as a result of electromagnetic influences. After all, neg-ion machines create ions, don't they, yet they are not giving off x-rays to do so.

If the impact of negative ions on organic life is beneficial, the understanding of its mechanisms must also be at a subatomic level. As the molecular biologist understands more about the way our cells use electromagnetic charges for oxygen transport, immune defence, and even perhaps for distant morphogenetic biocommunication or instruction for mitosis within the organism, then we shall start to get answers.

Dr Bernard Watson of Barts Hospital Medical Electronics has long recognized the benefits of neg-ions to asthmatic patients wearing synthetic garments. This anecdote (as related by Fred Soyka) gives a valuable lesson for those afflicted by asthma: 'Changing the immediately unhealthy ion environment to help the asthmatic means changing everything, clothes, sheets, furniture, just everything,' says Watson. When he talked in London to Soyka he told of one patient, a girl of 14, who had begun to suffer from severe migraine because of clothing – and then cured it herself. When she grew to adolescence and began to wear nylon bras and panties she began to suffer from headaches for the first time in her life. When she graduated to slips, nightdresses and nylon blouses she became a fully-fledged migraine sufferer.

Her local G.P. could offer neither explanation nor help, beyond suggesting the onset of menstruation as a cause. But the girl was bright enough to associate the clothes of blooming womanhood with her problem and promptly abandoned the underwear and nightdresses. Now her clothes are cotton, which is the only fibre which creates no charge at all, and of natural fibres like wool, which carry little charge of either kind.

Since in our modern world we mainly wear shoes, we are inevitably creating a potential difference between our bodies and the ground which is insulated from us by our own footwear: neg-ions accordingly find it difficult to gain access to our bodies, because we tend to repel the similar charges which they carry. Synthetic materials of all kinds – carpets, chairs, tables, sofas, curtains – can all upset the crucial ion balance, just as TV sets can. In fact, simply walking across a carpet with rubber shoes can develop a potential difference of 10,000 volts. This will ensure that we repel any friendly neg-ions and thus we often become physically, mentally, and emotionally depressed and irritable.

The importance of the ion effect may still be known to only few – prime ministers among them – but the gradual under-standing of organic life at this new 'electron'-ic level, and its implementation in our every day environment, could well have a large beneficial effect on the millions of patients currently crowding our doctors' surgeries. The doctors would feel better too, no doubt, from having such a burden removed.

7. The Amazing Ultraviolet Healing Machine

These views as usual pleased some more, others less; some chid and calumniated me, and laid it to me as a crime that I have dared to depart from the precepts . . . of all anatomists.

William Harvey (1578–1657),
discoverer of the circulation of the blood.

Three hundred years after William Harvey had passed away Richard Dawkins, in his book The Selfish Gene (1976), had some interesting things to say about the haemoglobin in our blood:

Haemoglobin is a modern molecule, used to illustrate the principle that atoms tend to fall into stable patterns. The point that is relevant here is that, before the coming of life on earth, some rudimentary evolution of molecules could have occurred by ordinary processes of physics and chemistry. There is no need to think of design, or purpose, or directness. If a group of atoms in the presence of energy falls into a stable pattern, it will stay that way.

Often our evolutionary past holds clues to the future.

In looking forward to the age of electromedicine, one has to admit that until antibiotics (some of us are still able to remember the crude doses of those yellow penicillin lozenges) took the medical stage by storm at the end of the Second World War, there was a definite trend towards electromagnetic energy applications in medical treatment. One striking example of this comes from a half-forgotten technique called haemo-irradiation, which appears to have succeeded where conventional chemotherapeutic methods failed.

In June 1934 Dr Virgil Hancock and E. K. Knott published in an obscure Pennsylvanian medical journal, North West Medicine, their experiences with a novel kind of treatment of pyogenic (pus-making) infections. With the aid of a specially-designed machine they irradiated some of their patients' blood with ultraviolet light and then replaced it in their bodies. The process of re-infusing someone with their own blood is known as autotransfusion, but no one had ever tried it in conjunction with UV before.

Their rationale was that blood infections are often caused by microbes or bacteria, as well as viruses, and UV is a well-known bacteriocidal agent. UV also activates sterol chemicals into vitamin D, an important vitamin produced only by sunlight, a deficiency of which can lead to rickets. Moreover UV is known to increase cell permeability and the blood's ability to transport oxygen. Finally Otto Rahn and others like Fritz Albert Popp noticed that normal blood actually radiates tiny amounts of UV, whereas in toxic and septic cases these radiations are absent. All these UV effects are generally beneficial, reasoned the two men, and though they could not explain why that should be, decided to try the treatment where all else had failed.

The results were encouraging. In those days penicillin and antibiotics had not reached volume production of today, so septicaemia and acute haemolytic infections were still a serious hazard. The new UV treatment was called the Knott technic after its inventor. By 1940 a number of Pennsylvanian hospitals and elsewhere had tried it out, with amazing success. Eager to tell the world of this new and promising discovery, they cooperated in setting up an exhibit at the 1940 American Medical Association Convention in New York, and presented a number of papers at the convention describing the successes of what they now called haemo-irradiation therapy.

Dr E. W. Rebbeck, the General Surgeon from Shadyside Hospital, Pittsburgh, describing thirteen cases of puerperal sepsis, could not have been more enthusiastic:

The thirteen charts and histories here cited represent the total number of cases of puerperal sepsis treated at the Hospital, [he began] . . . The results we obtained were gratifying. Our experience with this form of therapy has been wide enough to indicate its usefulness as a valuable adjunct to the treatment of various pathologies.

He then described the cases in detail, of which the following is one example:

Case One: Mrs M. age 41, a negro, was admitted on November 21st 1938 and discharged on December 23rd 1938. She was referred by Dr P. J. Mccomb, diagnosis, puerperal sepsis (acute septic endometritis). The patient was admitted November 21st 1938 for delivery. Temperature, pulse, and respirations were normal. Routine urinalysis was normal. Red blood count 3,980,000, hemoglobin 70 per cent, white cells, 10,100, – 90 per cent neutrophiles –. [My comment: this presumably meant that there were only about 1000 of the other types of white blood cells, including CD4 lymphocytes, which is much too low for comfort].

. . . consultation was held and a Porro Caesarian section performed because of a fibromyoma present in the cervical region. The diagnosis from the tissue examination showed acute septic endometritis and metritis. Sulfanilamide was started immediately and continued for four days or until November 28th inclusive, in doses of 100gr. the first day and 60 gr. for the next three days. Despite this therapy her temperature reached 104.8 deg. F. by November 28th.

The sulfanilamide therapy was stopped and blood irradiation therapy instituted. Her temperature gradually receded until December 4, with a marked improvement in her general condition. There was a gradual rise in temperature during the next two days, reaching a peak of 101.4 degrees F. on December 6. At this time another blood transfusion was given. From this point on she made an uneventful convalescence, being discharged from the hospital on December 23rd, apparently in good condition.

The accompanying chart showed that the UV irradiations were of only 190 and 120 cc of her blood respectively. Other cases cited by Dr Rebbeck were similar complication arising from septic conditions during childbirth, and one is left with the impression that without the treatment the patients may well have died. Dr Rebbeck concluded:

Our conclusions in the use of hemo-irradiation are:

1. The exposure of autotransfused blood to ultraviolet spectral energy, as outlined by the Knott technic, is a valuable and safe adjunct to the practise of medicine and surgery.

2. The biochemical background on this type of treatment is extensive and makes its use logical in indicated cases.

3. A definite reduction in toxicity is achieved.

4. In the treatment of puerperal sepsis it is invaluable.

Other applications of haemo-irradiation were not far behind: George Miley MD, DSc, a doctor at the Hahnemann Medical College, Philadelphia, found it worked to heal non-healing wounds, and reported this in the American Journal of Surgery in September 1944:

There occurs in a very low percentage of individuals who have recovered from the immediate effects of wounds a failure in healing, despite the very best local treatment plus normal supportive measures such as infusions, transfusions, rest, and adequate diet. This failure is apparently due to the absence in such individuals of a specific resistance factor, intrinsic in nature and of unknown character, often referred to as a general resistance factor.

In 1944 the new science of immunology was very little developed, so Miley's terms for immune defence sound somewhat quaint today. But there was nothing quaint about the results he achieved:

Acting on the belief that a normal ultraviolet balance might be absent in such individuals and that a resultant ultraviolet deprivation might be closely connected with the absence of the necessary specific resistance factor which regulates normal wound healing, we have in the last five years applied to six individuals with non-healing wounds the Knott technic of ultraviolet blood therapy. The duration of the non-healing wound in each of these individuals up to the time of the use of this method varied from five months to six years.

The rapid appearance of wound healing in and the recovery of all six of these individuals in a most convincing fashion has led us to believe that possibly ultraviolet deprivation played some part in the persistent failure of the normal healing process to appear in each instance.

Like his colleague Rebbeck, George Miley then detailed each of the cases. Here is one example:

Case Five: Rev. M.W. age 38, was admitted to the hospital November 29, 1939 following an automobile accident. Physical examination revealed fracture of the right femur and severe lacerations of the right forearm involving the whole extensive surface of the forearm, with an associated severance of the extensor pollicis longus tendon. The tendon was repaired immediately on admission and healed quite well. The patient's general condition improved and he recovered from the acute effects of his accident fairly well.

In this patient, however, despite all known general and local therapy, there occurred a non-union of the right femur and a failure to heal of the extensively lacerated area on the right forearm. This condition persisted for approximately five months, at the end of which time ultraviolet blood irradiation therapy was given this patient and within a week following this healthy granulation tissue appeared for the first time at the base of the lacerated wound in the right forearm. The wound began to close rapidly one week after irradiation, and was healed completely in eighteen days . . . The patient was discharged on May 21 1940 with the clinical signs of union of the fracture on the right femur almost complete and with the patient himself in apparently good condition.

Miley was probably not satisfied with his attempts to explain the mechanisms of interaction between the UV irradiation and the cells of the patients in his care. By 1941 he had assembled 103 cases of another disease state, pyogenia, which is the suppuration of tissues with pus. He had also been collecting some of the literature detailing the curative properties of UV light. In April 1941, on the occasion of the New York State's Annual Medical Society meeting he was invited to present his findings.

Having mentioned the detoxification of snake venom by UV light, its vasodilation, photosensitization, and related properties, and the improvement in oxygen transport from UV irradiation of the blood, he recorded many examples of the new wonder treatment, together with further details of the actual parameters of the irradiation.

The amount of blood to be irradiated rarely exceeds 300 cc.

he explained. The blood is passed through a chamber with a quartz window, and the UV source is 1 cm away from it. The exposure formula used was A = KW where A is the amount of blood in cc., K is a constant, 1.5 in this case, and W is the patient's weight in pounds. Time of exposure was the time required for 1 cc. of blood to pass through the Knott irradiation chamber while exposed to the UV radiation. The wavelengths used ranged from 239.9 nm to 365.4 nm (they used Angstroms as a measure in those days), and the power densities seemed very high, ranging from 41,000 mW/cm^2 to 1538,000 mW/cm^2.

In reading down the list of 103 patients treated by Miley, what is most staggering is that as well as curing 100 per cent of the early disease conditions (20 cases) and 98 per cent of the moderately advanced diseases (47 cases), the technique also cured 17 out of 36 'apparently moribund' patients, for example:

A man aged 52, was referred to the Hahnemann Hospital by Dr L. Bower. A diagnosis of acute gangrenous appendix, generalized peritonitis complicated by paralytic ileus and lobar pneumonia, was made. The patient was admitted on December 2, 1938, suffering from acute abdominal shock and giving a history of acute abdominal pain with nausea and vomiting, twenty four hours prior to admission. A physical examination revealed the probable presence of acute appendicitis. A routine urinalysis was negative. There were 20,250 leukocytes of which 89 per cent were neutrophils. He was operated upon on December 2 and a gangrenous appendix was removed. Appendectomy was followed by colostomy via lumen of the base of the appendix. A penrose drain was inserted, the peritoneum was closed, and the skin wound was packed with iodoform gauze.

The day following the operation he apparently developed right-sided atelectasis accompanied by dyspnoea. His temperature rose to 102 deg. F. On December 5 the patient was placed in an oxygen tent and later that evening an abdominal distention was noticed and his temperature rose to 103 deg. F. No peristalsis could be found and a diagnosis of acute widespreading peritonitis was made. Prontosil was started, 20 cc daily. On December 6 the peristalsis remained absent, and a blood transfusion was given. This was repeated December 8. The patient became more and more dyspneic, and prontosil was stopped; his toxic symptoms increased; rales were heard over a widespread pulmonary area; and increasing leg and ankle edema became apparent. On December 9 he became markedly cyanotic, dyspnea became advanced, abdominal distention increased, he apparently was succumbing to an overwhelming toxemia, secondary to his peritonitis, paralytic ileus, and intrapulmonary complications.

Blood irradiation therapy was instituted on December 9. A few minutes later the patient's cyanosis had disappeared, his skin became quite pink, his dyspnea was markedly relieved, and he slept well throughout the night following blood irradiation therapy, the first sleep he had had since admission . . .

Two more irradiations were performed.

On the following day his general clinical condition was greatly improved. His abdomen was almost normally soft, and peristalsis, which had disappeared the previous day, was re-established. From this point onwards he began to improve. It was possible for the first time to remove gradually all drainage tubes. On December 20 secondary suture of the abdominal wound was done, and the patient continued to convalesce uneventfully and was discharged from hospital in apparently fine condition on January 14 1939.

Miley noted that

In patients receiving blood irradiation for acute pyogenic infection, and having abnormal hemoglobin, red cell, white cell values before treatment all these disappear, changing to normal following hemoirradiation. We have been unable to find delayed harmful effects of any nature in over 1000 applications of the Knott technic of ultraviolet blood irradiation.

Studies by Miley and Rebbeck continued to appear in journals like the Review of Gastroenterology and Archives of Physical Therapy during the next few years, all reporting great success, often in hopeless cases. By June 1947 Miley and a colleague Dr Jens Christensen reviewed their progress at the annual convention of the National Gastroenterological Association at Atlantic City, and shocked their audience with the additional revelation that the treatment also worked on viruses. Miley's opening statement was in sharp contradistinction to the earlier traditional diffidence with which most medical researchers are imbued:

Inasmuch as at present there is no effective method of controlling serious virus or virus-like infections, any method which has shown even a preliminary encouraging trend in this direction must be considered. Ultraviolet blood irradiation therapy has, in our experience, shown such a trend in the 79 consecutive cases in which we have used this method.

Having briefly re-explained the haemo-irradiation technique, he predated the evolving science of immunology by several decades, pointing out that 'these favourable clinical results have been shown to be due to a tremendous and rapid rise in the patient's own resistance to infection rather than to any direct bacteriocidal effect, though ultraviolet rays are lethal to all the common coccal bacteria'. In other words it improved their immune defence systems.

As Miley begins to unfold the categories of disease which he has cured by means of the Knott technic, the implications of this method for treating serious immune deficits slowly dawn:

Forty three cases of early primary atypical or virus pneumonia (they had not heard of pneumocystis carinii pneumonia in those days), poliomyelitis, herpes simplex, zoster, and ophthalmaticus were treated, and forty three recovered. Even today the herpes virus is not regarded as eradicable once it has infected a human being, though it may remain asymptomatic for years. 27 cases of moderately advanced cases of these, including one of mumps, were treated and all recovered. Finally 9 cases of atypical or virus pneumonia and bulbospinal poliomyelitis where the patient was apparently moribund were treated and all but one recovered.

Even then Miley had to admit bafflement of how his amazing technique actually worked:

The mechanism by which this method acts is not definitely known, but it seems highly probable that the resistance of the host is raised rapidly and efficiently by a direct stimulating and energizing effect following the intravenous introduction of ultraviolet energy. Inasmuch as there exists no other method of favourably influencing or controlling virus or virus like infections, ultraviolet blood irradiation therapy, in the light of clinical experience to date, deserves a wide application in the treatment of such infections.

Dr G. J. P. Barger was in the audience on that day, and added his own experience to that of Miley:

In my experience in giving 2,500 ultraviolet blood irradiation treatments, I am glad to be able to confirm Dr Miley's conservative statements in regard to the efficacy of ultraviolet blood irradiation therapy in the treatment of atypical or virus pneumonia . . . in another viral disease, encephalitis, for which there has been inadequate therapy, I have three early cases of children treated by ultraviolet blood irradiation with surprisingly good results, which seem to be standing the test of time.

The three cases were diagnosed as meningoencephalitis, and encephalitis lethargica. Dr Barger was of the same mind as to the way the treatment worked:

Ultraviolet blood irradiation, in my analysis of its effects, mobilizes the defensive mechanisms of the body on a very high level, so that these mechanisms work with markedly increased efficiency in performing their normal functions of combatting microinvaders of body fluids and tissues. Dr Miley has excellently stated this idea in different words.

The results of ultraviolet blood irradiation in the hands of different men have been so consistent, and the results in the treatment of virus diseases for which nothing else had been available, so good to those who have had a chance to watch the results closely, that it seems an opportunity should open up for an extensive trial of this therapy not only in all the virus diseases but also in the rickettsial diseases, which has been equally lacking in effective therapy.

Summing up his presentation, Miley was able to say:

We know, all of us who began this work some eight or nine years ago, that no harmful effects have been observed. If there had been anything deleterious, at least the deleterious effects would have been limited to the first three or four of us doing this work. Now we know there are no longstanding deleterious effects, so that the apparatus can be distributed safely on a widespread basis.

To date over 60,000 blood irradiations have been done in this country including over 10,000 of ours, and the workers are in very close agreement with what has been published to date.

So what happened to this promising technique? In Peter Radetsky's otherwise excellent book on the emerging age of viruses neither Miley, nor Rebbeck, nor the Knott technic, nor haemo-irradiation get a single mention. The invention seems somehow to have disappeared from the face of medical science. I cannot trace its manufacturers, the Scientific Equipment Manufacturing Company in Seattle, and though the beneficial health effects of UV are well reported for disorders like psoriasis, their application to viral infections particularly to AIDS, if AIDS is caused by a virus, that is, has never been made in any meaningful way.

In the intervening years antibiotics have more conveniently carried out many of the bacteriocidal duties of Knott's technic, giving rise to some of our largest industrial companies who have benefited from the discovery. But there are many cases where antibiotics have proved ineffective, and indeed they are ineffective against viruses too. Dr Eberhard from Philadelphia provides an example from his casebook:

During the summer of 1946 a woman patient spent the entire time on a ranch in the Western United States. She drank abundantly of milk from cows, that so far as she knew, were not inspected for the usual infections. No goat milk was taken, notwithstanding that many goats were in evidence. On her return to New York she became markedly fatigued, had anorexia, lost ten pounds in weight, and noted a temperature between 101 and 102 degrees F. She stated she had been given penicillin by mouth without results, after which she was placed on sulfonamides, all without result.

When she reported to me in Philadelphia she had the appearance of a woman quite ill. While in the hospital the usual laboratory tests were made such as red, white and differential counts, all of which revealed a decided secondary anaemia and an increased leucocyte count ranging between 12,000 and 15,000 with polymorphonuclear cells 78-80 per cent, large and small lymphocytes 20 per cent. Eosinophils 2 per cent. Agglutination tests for typhoid, paratyphoid A and B, Brucellosis, and proteus X19 were all negative . . .

Considering that this patient had been given penicillin, sulfonamides, and streptomycin, I advised intravenous blood irradiation at Dr Miley's clinic. No vaccine therapy was administered or other medication was given. Within four days after the first irradiation the temperature began falling by lysis, and on the seventh day it returned to normal. From that time on the patient improved generally. The macular rash disappeared, and a weight gain was noted. She was given a blood irradiation weekly for six weeks and one every month for four months. When last seen, she had completely recovered and had regained her normal weight.

Not content with a state of affairs which allows such an important discovery in electrohealing to fade from view, my laboratory is now in course of developing an instrument which is capable of doing what the Knott technic did so many years before. We no longer need to employ the mercury vapour lamps which Miley used, for technology has passed on. Sadly however even if we have completed the engineering the instrument can only be used if approved, and approvals might take a decade, involving animal trials, clinical trials, and the close supervision of an ethical committee before it can be made available for hospital use. These checks and balances are necessary to protect the public as far as possible from any long term hazards, of which thalidomide remains an indelible example. Sooner or later however, clinical trials in this type of equipment must take place on AIDS patients, I predict.

Meanwhile it is useful to try and understand the mechanisms underlying the technique of ultraviolet blood irradiation. This begins with the constituents of the blood cell itself.

Blood is a most fascinating tissue. Only in the seventeenth century did Harvey discover that our blood circulates around the body. When he had put forward this innovative notion in 1616 he was immediately thought mad. A friend of his, John Aubrey, wrote:

I have heard him say that after his booke of the Circulation of the Blood came out, that he fell mightily in his practize, and twas beleeved by the vulgar that he was crack-brained; and all itians were against his position and envyed him.

blood, as we now know, is pumped by the heart from the lungs where it collects oxygen, straight to the brain, which consumes nearly a third of that oxygen in sending out electromagnetic instructions like a radio transmitter and electrochemical reactions which send nervous impulses down the spinal cord, to the cells of our body. The brain has first call on oxygen as the blood meanders around the arteries, delivering oxygen to our muscles, collecting carbon dioxide in its place, and returning through the veins to lungs to expel the carbon dioxide collect more oxygen, and through the heart again to repeat its journey.

All the many kinds of blood cells have a limited life and have to be regenerated from haematopoietic stem cells made in the bone marrow. The red blood cells or erythrocytes contain no DNA and are thus blind to signals, but they are filled almost exclusively with haemoglobin assemblies which are designed to change their magnetic fields when collecting or depositing oxygen and carbon dioxide, just as an electro-magnet can pick up, and drop a pin. These red blood cells cannot divide without DNA, and they wear out so quickly that they have to be generated at the furious rate of two million each second!

Dawkins tells how the haemoglobin within red blood cells 'is not a haphazard approximate pattern but a definite invariant structure, identically repeated, with not a twig nor a twist out of place, over six thousand million million million times in an average human body . . . Haemoglobin "thornbushes" are springing into their preferred shape in your body at a rate of about four hundred million million per second, and others are being destroyed at the same rate'.

Red blood cells disgorge their original nucleus just before they leave their home in the bone marrow, and only exist for about 120 days in circulation. By contrast there is only one white blood cell for every thousand red cells, and there are many different kinds of white blood cells, all of which have at least one nucleus. One class of white cells, the granulocytes, only lasts a day or two, whereas some types of lymphocyte can circulate around the blood and lymphatic system for years. Smaller than all of them are the platelets, which again are without a nucleus and sensitive to magnetism. This attraction to magnetism helps them to stick together at wound sites and help with the formation of healing tissues.

The way they do this is that there are four haems or iron atoms attached to four multi-horseshoe shaped globins. The globins are polarized: one end of their chain congregates acids while the other end congregates basic amino ends, and since the bends are more or less parallel their magnetic fields cancel out all around the haem, protecting its magnetic character. The single iron atoms of each haem, like all iron atoms has five unpaired electrons in their outer shells.

This arrangement means that the four haems collectively could choose to have all its electrons spinning in equilibrium, (say two pairs around each atom and the remaining four paired together) or could have all twenty spinning in one plane and direction, which would create a net magnetic moment similar to a powerful magnet when all the haemoglobins in one red blood cell act cooperatively.

So haemoglobin can be thought of as paramagnetic (weakly magnetic) or diamagnetic (hardly magnetic). Normally its magnetism is minimal, but if exposed to high electric or magnetic field it tends to become magnetized, and once in that condition its oxygen transport capability is reduced. There is another effect too. The white blood cells include three types of lymphocyte which are magnetotropic. This attraction to magnetic fields arises from the ferritin they carry on their cell membrane surface.

By adjusting the ferritin and their other cell surface proteins lymphocytes are provoked to turn themselves into magnets by antigenic influences, and they can thus propel themselves speedily towards any source of magnetism. In our bodies magnetic fields are present at open wound sites, or where the myelin of a nerve fibre has come away exposing the nerve inside, or where bones press together from our own weight, causing piezoelectricity.

That lymphocytes are heavily influenced by electro-magnetism is shown by the fact that they have a circadian cycle: there are more of them in evidence in the bloodstream at midnight, when the sun's radiation is at its least, and less at sunrise when the sun comes around the earth. Similarly red blood cells flocculate more or less in a liquid according to the influence of the moon which changes the ion content of the earth on a monthly basis. We have all evolved with these natural magnetic fields, and our life patterns fit well with them.

he newly-created artificial electromagnetic fields of modern life can disrupt these established patterns and the structures in our bodies which are evolved to work with them, with damaging results on our health. AIDS patients for example lose their lymphocyte circadian rhythm very early in their disorder, which gives us a clue that there is a magnetic effect lurking somewhere in the background of AIDS aetiology. If so, then perhaps Miley's technique could be of benefit there too.

Magnetism is sometimes clearly unwanted, so the body heats up its blood as a technique for lowering its magnetism. Heat causes all electrons to get excited and break off from their existing spin states, so if the spin states were all aligned before, by applying heat they become disoriented and lose their magnetism. Iron loses its magnetism almost completely at a temperature level called the Curie point. When we have a fever, what we are doing is heating up the blood to reduce the alien magnetic influences being caused by infecting agents. Disease is therefore a kind of war of competing radiations.

Blood cells play a role in this homeostasis, keeping the body's temperature at the right level for magnetic equilibrium as well as for chemical equilibrium so that the chemical reactions in our body take place at the right speed.

If our blood has become over-magnetized however, the lymphocytes become inhibited and cannot carry out so well their cytotoxic (cell killing) role, tending to congregate in the blood stream and not paying attention to other foreign magnetic signals from wounds, invading organisms, the healing brain, and other sources. Leukaemia is one result: our blood actually looks milky because there are so many lymphocytes in it, though locked onto the red cells they cannot carry out their job and are incompetent. Another result is that the blood itself, being magnetized cannot carry oxygen so efficiently, so we feel tired, achy, and off colour.

The action of UV in the Knott technique is manifold: ultraviolet radiation acts directly on the electrons in the haems, vibrating them at about 10^{15} times a second and thereby shaking them from their spin state back to the unpaired state which is their normal functioning mode. Once the erythrocytes' magnetism is degaussed so to speak, the lymphocytes no longer hang around the attracting blood cells, but get on with their twenty four hour job of destroying foreign microbes, and the blood gets back to carrying oxygen around the body more efficiently again. That is roughly how Miley's haemo-irradiation technique works at a molecular biological level.

Of course, the UV also has a bacteriocidal effect, which acts by literally shaking the hydrogen bonds of bacteria apart inside their DNA and killing them instantly. This happens to some of the white blood cells too, but UV cannot do that kind of damage to the red blood cells because they have no DNA to damage. Lymphocytes and other cells inside the body are subsequently repaired in the dark in a process appropriately called 'dark repair' (i.e. when there is no EM fields around at visible light frequencies), whereas the bacteria, which have no central controlling signal cannot be repaired in this way, unless they have really taken a hold on the territory and are cooperatively generating large and strong signals of their own kind.

This kind of explanation is really very new, and takes not only the electrochemical but the electromagnetic qualities of life molecules into account. Using this approach a number of biological mysteries can be explained, but that is another story. The main thing, like Miley's technique, is that it works and we should be using it in the medicine of the future.

Another way of demagnetizing any material is to heat it. One of the effects of exposing blood to electromagnetic energy is that its haem becomes slightly magnetized. Could the magnetized blood be fogging the signals being transmitted to the lymphocytes enable them to distinguish between pathogenic and friendly cells? If this were so, then no sieve would be small enough to resolve pathogens in the blood. And by demagnetizing or degaussing the blood the symptoms should disappear. As it happens there was an AIDS patient recently who as a last resort had his blood drawn out and heated up to 108 degrees Fahrenheit before being replaced. The AIDS symptoms disappeared in just a few days afterwards.

The patient, 33 year old Carl Crawford, was treated in Atlanta, Georgia by Drs William Logan and Kenneth Alonso, formerly of the Atlantic Hospital. They had developed this heating treatment of the blood since 1981, but Logan's paper describing his results submitted to the Journal of the American Medical Association (JAMA) was rejected on the grounds of insufficient research. Hyperthermia would have the effect of demagnetizing the blood, since heating is one way of accomplishing this, the others being percussion and degaussing.

The opposition which met Logan's research has virtually driven him underground, as well as the attendant publicity incited by his former colleague Alonso. Logan has nevertheless set up a secret facility in Belize where he continues to treat cases, and his first paper has now been published in a Swedish medical journal. The results are encouraging, to say the least, though Logan was amazed to learn from me the possible mechanism whereby his treatment became effective, since no one had thought of the demagnetizing implications of heating the blood before.

I discuss the implications of such an approach for serious immune deficits in another forthcoming book. My message in this one is to point to the way in which electromagnetic energies, sometimes at very weak or subtle levels, can have enormous consequences for our health, both for worse and for better, and that we should heed how we allow our bodies to be exposed to electromagnetic influences for which we are not biologically prepared by evolution.

We have had the benefit of electrical energy for little more than one lifetime in our evolutionary history: radio only since 1920; TV only since the early 1950s; satellite communications, car phones, fax, TV phones for only a few short years. The discoverer of the fractional horsepower motor which drives the world's washing machines and other electric appliances, Nikola Tesla, attracts more interest today from the American public than Mikhail Gorbachov the previous leader of the USSR, just one notch below Al Capone and three below Jesus, according to Encyclopaedia Britannica's Research Enquiry Service.

Nikola Tesla is not very well known even so: yet to him we owe the alternating current in our house wiring, remote control of TV sets, wireless communication, the incandescent light bulb, and a host of other innovations possibly even including x-rays. Least known of all of these, and in fact almost the only inventions from which he profited during his long and chequered lifetime, were little electrical devices for therapeutic heating:

'It occurred to me,' he wrote on December 23rd 1891, a few days over a century ago as I write, 'whether, with such apparatus properly prepared, it would not be possible for a skilled physician to find in it a means for the effective treatment of various types of disease. The heating will, of course, be superficial, that is, on the skin, and would result, whether the person operated on were dressed in thick clothes or whether reduced to nakedness. In fact, to put it broadly, that a person entirely nude at the North Pole might keep himself comfortably warm in this manner. Without vouching for the results, which must be determined by experience and observation, I can at least warrant the fact that heating would occur by this method of subjecting the human body to bombardment by alternating currents of high potential and frequency such as I have long worked with. It is only reasonable to expect that some of the effects will be wholly different from those obtainable with the old familiar therapeutic methods generally used. Whether they would all be beneficial or not remains to be proved.'

Once again Tesla has proved himself a prophet of our age. It is becoming an age which stands in certain need of such therapies.

Meanwhile we should feel again, with deeper insight, the gentle healing warmth of the early summer's sun upon our skin, the paleness of the full moon above us, slicing through thin diaphanous clouds below the invisible mantle of a delicate ionosphere protecting us from the harsher radiations of the sun's energy; and the eternal stars, all held in their timeless course by the very same invisible forces with which we, like children, have begun idly to play for the first time in our planet's history.

Let us hope that we use these new found toys wisely.

Select Bibliography

R. Abraham & A. Liboff, 'Search for Ion-cyclotron Resonance in an Na+-Transport System', *BEMS.* 12: pp.77–83 (1991).

Albert Abrams, *New Concepts in Diagnosis and Treatment*, Philopolis Press, San Francisco, (1916).

Albert Abrams, (Defamatory Articles on him) *Sci. Amer* Nov 23 p.306 Dec 23 p.392, (1924).

Albert Abrams, *The Blues* [splanchnic neurasthenia] *causes and cure* [Early reference to M.E.], New York (1908).

E. D. Acheson, 'Multiple Sclerosis, A reappraisal', In McAlpine, Churchill Livingstone, London (1972).

G. Adams, 'An Essay on Electricity, Explaining the Principles of that Useful Science and Describing the Instruments Contrived Either to Illustrate the Theory, or Render the Practice Entertaining' (ed. W. Jones), Dillon & Co, London 482-575, (1799).

Jad Adams, *The HIV Myth*, McMillan, London, pp.12–14 (1989).

W. R. Adey, 'Organisation of brain tissue: is the brain a noisy processor?', *Int. J. Neurosci.* 3: pp.271–284 (1972).

W. R. Adey, 'Evidence for cooperation mechanisms in the susceptibility of cerebral tissue to environmental and intrinsic electric fields.' In *Functional Linkage in Biomolecular Systems* (ed. F. O. Schmidt, D. M. Schneider *et al.*,) New York, Raven 1975, pp.325-42.

W. R. Adey, 'Biophysical and metabolic bases of cooling effects on cortical membrane potentials in the cat', *Exp. Neurol.* 42: pp.113–140 (1974).

W. R. Adey, 'Brain interactions with weak electric and magnetic fields', *Neurosci. Res. prog. Bull.* 14: pp.7–16 (1977)

E. D. Adrian & B. C. H. Matthews, 'The interpretation of

potential waves in the cortex', *Jnl. of Physiol.* 81: pp.440–471 (1934).

Adrian & Yamaguwa, 'The origin of the Berger Rhythm', *Brain*, 58: pp.323–51 (1935).

Bruce Alberts, Dennis Bray, *et al*, *Molecular Biology of the Cell*, Garland Publishing, N.Y. (1983).

W. C. Alvarez, 'The Migraine Scotoma as studied in 618 Persons', *Amer. Jnl. Ophth.* 49: pp.489 (1960).

P. Andersen and S. A. Andersson, '*Brain/Hypothalamus. The Physiological basis of The Alpha Rhythm*, Appleton Century Crofts, N.Y. (1986).

E. W. Anderson, *Animals as Navigators*, Bodley Head, London (1983).

Anon, 'How does acupuncture work?', *British Medical Journal* 283: pp.746–48 (1981).

Anon (Editorial in Lancet), 'The Cardiac Reflex of Abrams', *Lancet:* 29 August (1903).

Archer (1978), 'Geomagnetism, Cancer, Weather and Cosmic Radiation', *Health Physics*, Pergamon Press Vol 34 (March) pp.237–47 (1978).

Deiter Aschoff, 'Biologische Wirking von Edelstemen', *Proc. Intl. Arbeitskleises fur Geobiologie*, Veflag Metir Wissen, Dusseldorf (1988).

Kaethe Bachler, *Earth Radiation: The startling discoveries of a dowser*, Wordmasters, Manchester (1989).

Cleveland Backster, 'Evidence of a primary perception in plant life', *Intl. Jnl. Parapsych.* 10 (4): pp.329–48N (1968).

Laurence E. Badgley, 'A new method for locating acupuncture points and body field distortions', *American Jnl. of Acupuncture* 12, No. 3 pp.219–228 (1984).

Baranski, S., 'Effects of microwaves on the reactions of the white blood cell system', *Acta Physiol Pol.* 23: p.685 (1972).

Baranski & Czerski P., *Biologic effects of microwaves*, Stroudsberg Dowden, Hutchison & Ross, 1976.

A. T. Barker & L. F. Jaffe, *et al.*, 'Lateral voltage gradients near mammalian skin wounds' *A.M. Zoolog*, 21 (4) pp.998–1007 (1981).

A. T. Barker & M. J. Lunt, 'The effects of pulsed magnetic fields of the type used in the stimulation of bone fracture healing', *Clin. Phys. Physiol Meas*, 4: pp.1–27 (1983).

R. D. Barnard, M. Triggs, 'The Corpus Callosum in Multiple Sclerosis', *Jnl. of Neurology, Neurosis & Psychol* Vol 37.

pp.1259–64 (1974).

Frank Barnes, Howard Wachtel, *et al.*, 'Use of wiring configurations and wiring codes for estimating externally generated electric and magnetic fields', *Bioelectromagnetics*, 10 (1): pp.13–21 (1989).

P. Barnes, J. L. Finney, *et al.* 'Coop effects in simulated water computer simulations show formation of long-range coop effects' *Nature* 282, pp.459–64 (1979).

M. Barnothy, 'Reduction of Radiation mortality through magnetic pre-treatment', *Nature* 200, pp.279 (1963a).

M. Barnothy & J. Barnothy, 'Biological Effects of Magnetic Fields', *Medical Physics* 3. Yearbook Pubs., Chicago (1960).

Madeleine Barnothy, *Biological Effects of Magnetic Fields*, Plenum Press, NY (1964).

James Barr, *Abrams Methods of Diagnosis and Treatment* William Heinneman (Medical Books) Ltd, London (1925).

C. A. L. Bassett, 'The development of pulsed electromagnetic fields (PEMFS) for ununited fractures and arthrodeses', *Clin. Plast. Surg.* 12: pp.259–77 (1985).

C. A. L. Bassett, *et al.*, 'The effect of PEMFs on cellular calcium and calcification of non-unions', In *Electrical Properties of Bone and Cartilage: Experimental Effects and Clinical Applications* (Eds. C. T. Brighton, J. Black, S. R. Pollack) Grune & Stratton, New York; pp.427–41 (1979).

Antoine Beauchamp, *Microzyme Theory of Disease*, Univ. of Toulouse (1816–1908).

R. O. Becker & Gary Seldon, *The Body Electric: Electromagnetism and the Foundation of Life*, Morrow, N.Y. (1985).

R. O. Becker, *Mechanisms of Growth Control*, C. C. Thomas, N.Y. (1981).

R. O. Becker & Andrew Marino, *Electromagnetism and Life*, Suny Press, Albany, NY (1982).

R. O. Becker, *Cross Currents: the perils of electropollution, the promise of electromedicine*, Jeremy P. Tarcher, Los Angeles, 1990.

Jacques Benveniste, 'Human Basophil degranulation triggered by very dilute antiserums against IgE', *Nature* 333 pp.816–8 (1988).

R. H. C. Bentall & D. Beard, 'Effects of 26MHz on skin wound healing in the guinea pig', *BEMS Ann Mtg.* San Antonio, Texas, June 1990.

Valerie Beral, S. Evans *et al.*, 'Malignant Melanoma and

exposure to fluorescent lighting at work', *Lancet* (2). pp.290–93, 7th August, 1982.

Valerie Beral and Michel Coleman, 'Review of epidemiological studies on the health and safety effects of working with electricity generation and transmission equipment', *Intl. J. Epidemiol.*, 17 pp.1–13 (1988).

M. Berg, I. Langlet, 'Defective video displays, shields and skin problems', *Lancet* 4th April p.800 (1987).

Hans Berger, 'Uber das Elektrenkephalogram des Menschen.' First Report. *Arch. fur Psychiatr. & Nervenkrankheit* 87, pp.527–70 (1929).

Hans Berger, *Psyche*, Gustav Fischer (publ), Jena (1940).

Christopher Bird, *Divining*, MacDonald and Jane's, London and Sydney (1980).

B. R. Bloom, Immunological Changes in Multiple Sclerosis, *Nature* 287, pp.275–76 (1980).

R. B. Borgens, J. W. Vanable & L. F. Jaffe, 'Bioelectricity regeneration: large currents leave the stumps of regenerating newt limbs', *PNAS* 74, p.4528 (1977).

W. E. Boyd, 'Biochemical and biological evidence of the activity of high potencies', *Brit. Hom. J.* 44, pp.6–44 (1954).

W. E. Boyd, M.D., 'Recent Research on the Relation of cerebrum Electro-Physical phenomena to homoeopathy (with special reference to the work of Dr Abrams of San Francisco), *British Homoeopathic Congress*, London (1922, 1923).

R. J. Bray & P. Relough, *Sunspots*, Chapman & Hall, London (1964).

Paul Brodeur, *The Zapping of America*, W.W. Norton, NY (1977).

Paul Brodeur, *Currents of Death*, Simon Schuster, NY (1990).

T. H. Bullock, 'Electromagnetic sensing in fish', *Neurosci. Res. Program Bull.*, 15 (1) pp.17–22 (1977).

R. Cadossi, 'In Vitro and In Vivo Effects of Electromagnetic Fields: Their Possible Role in the Development of New Strategies for Cancer Treatment', *J. Bioelect.* 9(2) pp.197–203 (1990).

Rachel Carson, *Silent Spring*, Hamish Hamilton, London (1963).

I. Chanarin, M. Brozovic, *et al. Blood and Its Diseases*, Churchill Livingstone, Edinburgh, 2nd ed. (1980).

Margaret Cheney, *Tesla: Man out of Time*, Prentice Hall, Englewood Cliffs, London (1981).

P. Conti, G. E. Gigante, *et al.*, 'Reduced, mitogenic stimulation of human lymphocytes by extremely low frequency electromagnetic fields', *FEBS* 162 (1) pp.156–60 (1983).

George Washington Crile, *The Phenomena of Life: a radio-electric interpretation*, Heinemann, U.S. (1936).

Francis Crick, *On Protein Synthesis*, Symposium of Society, Exp. Biol. 12: 138 (1958).

Herbert Douglas, 'The strange role of dowsing in medicine', *The Banner*, Bennington, Mass, Dec 7 & 8 (1976).

L. E. Eeman, *Co-operative Healing. The curative properties of human radiations*, Frederick Muller Ltd., London (1947).

L. E. Eeman, *How do you sleep?* Author Partner Press Ltd. London (1939).

S. Fitton-Jackson, *et al.*, 'Effects of pulsed magnetic fields on acute tendon injuries', *BEMS*, San Francisco, 10 (1985).

H. Frohlich, 'Coherence in biology', *Coherent excitations in biological systems* (Ed. H. Frohlich and F. Kremer) Springer Verlag (1983).

William F. Ganong, *Review of Medical Physiology*, Lange Med. Pubs. Ca. 7th edit (1975).

R. G. Gibson, Sheila L. M. Gibson, *et al.*, 'Homœopathic therapy in rheumatoid arthritis: evaluation by double-blind clinical therapeutic trial, *BJ Clin. Pharm.* 9, p.453 (1980).

R. S. Gibson & W. F. Moroney, 'The effects of ELF magnetic fields on human performance', AD 005898, Namrl-1195 (Naval aerospace Res. Lab.), Pensacola, FL.

K. Giczi & A. Guseo, 'Treatment of headache by pulsating electromagnetic field: A preliminary report', *J. Bioelectricity* 7 (1): pp.125–6 (1988).

E. Del. Giudice, S. Doglia, *et al.* '*Raman spectroscopy and order in biological systems*', *Cell biophysics*, 6, pp.117–29 (1984).

A. Gmitrova, *et al.*, 'Biological effect of a magnetic field on laboratory animals (abstract)', *Journal of Bioelectricity* 7: pp.123–4 (1988).

A. Gmitrova & J. Gmitrova, 'Effect of a Permanent Magnetic Field on Blood Pressure Regulation', *J Bioelect*, 9(1) pp.79–83 (1990).

R. Goodman, C. A. L. Bassett, *et al.*, 'Pulsing electromagnetic fields induce cellular transcription', *Science* 220: pp.1283–4 (1983).

R. E. Granda & A. H. Frey, 'Human reaction to air ions. Part II', The effect of atmospheric ions on human behaviour.

Leo Gross, 'Bibliography of the biological effects of static magnetic fields in Barnothy M. (ed) 1964 q.v.

A. A. Gurwitsch, *et al.*, 'Registration of mitogenic radiation of animal tissue in vivo etc', *Nature* 206: pp.20–22 (1965).

Roza Hajdukovic, *et al.*, 'Increase of Stage 2 NREM Sleep In Chronic Insomniacs After 4 Week Treatment With Low Energy Emission Therapy', Abstracts: *BEMS* 12th Annual Meeting, San Antonio, Texas (1990).

Spencer Hamada, Van Andrew Davis III, *et al.*, 'Human white blood cells will actively migrate across a filter to the anode in a weak electric field', *BEMS* Ann Mtg. Salt Lake City, June 23–7 (1991).

M. Hamilton, 'Electroconvulsive therapy. Indications and contraindications', *Ann N.Y. Acad. Sci.* 462 pp.5–11 (1986).

V. K. Hancock & E. K. Knott, 'Irradiated Blood Transfusion in the treatment of infections', *Northwest Med.* 33: p.200 (1934).

Virgil K. Hancock, 'Treatment of blood stream infections with hemo-irradiation', *Amer. Jnl. Surgery* 58 (3): pp.336–44 (1942).

Alfred Haviland, 'The Geographical distribution of Disease in Great Britain', *Lancet* 25 Feb 1888, p.365.

Gerald S. Hawkins, *Stonehenge Decoded*, Souvenir Press (1966).

L. H. Hawkins, 'The influence of air ions, temperature, and humidity on selective well being and comfort', *Jnl. Environ. Psychol.* 1: pp.279–292 (1981).

S. M. Hinsull, E. L. Head & D. Bellamy, 'The effect of negative air ionization on the thymus glands of laboratory rats', *Jnl. of Biological Physics* II p.87–90 (1983).

R. E. Hope-Simpson, *Relationship of Influenza pandemics to sunspot cycles* (M. Kingsbourn, W. Lynn Smith eds), Charles C. Thomas, Springfield, Illinois (1974).

Sir Thomas Horder, *Preliminary communication to RSM*, Bale & Sons, Daniellson, London (1925).

F. Howard & Humphris, *The Electronic Reactions of Abrams*, Lancet: 176, 26 January (1924).

V. P. Kaznacheev, S. P. Shurin, *et al.*, 'Distant intercellular interactions in a system of two tissue cultures', *Psychoenergetic systems* 1: pp.141–2 (1976).

A. P. Krueger, 'Influences of air ions on certain physiological functions', *Med. Biometeorology-Weather, climate and the living organism*, Elsevier, Amsterdam, 1963.

A. P. Krueger, 'Air ion effects on the iron metabolism of barley', *Proc. Japan. Botanical Soc.*, 1965.

Georges Lakhovsky, *L'Oscillation Cellulaire*, Doin, Paris (1931).

G. Lakhovsky, *The Theory of Cancer based on the geological nature of the soil*, Revue Generale des Sciences, 15 October (1928).

Georges Lakhovsky, *The Secret of Life*, W. Heinemann (Medical Books) London (1939).

O. Larko & G. Swanbeck, Home Solarium Treatment of Psoriasis, *Br. Jnl. Dermatol.* 101 (3) p.13 (1979).

K. S. Lashley, *Brain Mechanisms & Intelligence*, University Chicago Press (1929).

V. V. Lednev, 'Possible Mechanism for the Influence of Weak Magnetic Fields on Biological Systems', *BEMS.* 12: pp.71–75 (1991).

Mario Lenzi, 'A report of a few recent experiments on the biologic effects of magnetic fields' *Radiol:* 35: pp.307–14 (1940).

A. Liboff, *et al.*, *'Time ranging magnetic fields: Effect on DNA synthesis'*, *Science* 223: pp.818–20 (1984).

A. R. Liboff, B. R. McLeod, *et al.*, 'Ion Cyclotron resonance effects of ELF fields in biological systems'. In *Extremely Low Frequency Electromagnetic fields: The question of cancer* (Eds. Bary Wilson, Richard Stevens, and Larry Anderson) Battelle, Richland, 1990.

R. P. Liburdy & R. L. Miller, 'Magnetic field interaction with calcium ion in the lymphocyte', Abstracts: Bioelectromagnetics 10th Annual Meeting. 19–23 June (1988).

R. Liburdy, 'RF radiation alters the immune system: Modulation of, T- and B- lymphocyte levels and cell-mediated immunocompetence by hyperthermic radiation', *Radiation Research*, 77: pp.34–46 (1979).

Karl E. Lotz, *Do you want to live Healthily?*, Paffrath-Druck KG Remscheid, W. Germany (1982).

R. A. Luben, *et al.*, 'Effects of electromagnetic stimuli on bone and bone cells in vitro', *Proc. Natl. Acad. Sci. U.S.A.* 79: pp.4180–4 (1982).

W. Ludwig, 'The scientific and physical aspects of MORA therapy in acupuncture', *Amer. J. Acu.* 15, p.129 (1987).

A. A. Marino (ed.), *Modern Bioelectricity*, New York: Marcel Dekker (1988).

Ronald Marks, *The Sun and Your Skin*, Macdonald Optima,

London (1988).

C. F. Mayers and J. A. Habeshaw, 'Depression of Phagocytosis – A Nonthermal Effect of Microwave Radiation, a potential hazard to health', *Int. Jnl. of Radiat. Biol.* 24: pp.449–61 (1973).

D. J. McGinty, *et al.*, *Brain Mechanisms of Sleep*, Raven Press, N.Y. (1985).

George Miley & P. M. Dunning, 'Ultraviolet Blood irradiation in acute virus and virus-type infections', *Rev, Gastroenterol* 15 (4): p.271 (1948).

George Miley, 'Ultraviolet Blood Irradiation Therapy in Acute Poliomyelitis', *Arch. Phys. Therapy* 25 p.651 (Nov 1944).

George Miley, 'Ultraviolet Irradiation of Auto-transferred Human Blood Studies in Oxygen Absorption Values', *Am Jnl. of Med. Sci.* 197: n. 6873 (June 1939).

George Miley, 'Treatment of eight cases of atypical pneumonia by ultraviolet blood irradiation', *Amer. Bacter. Soc.* (Penn Chapter) Feb (1943).

Jean Monro & Cyril Smith, 'The ultimate antidote?', *Jnl. Alt. & Comp. Med.* 23–25 June (1988).

K. Nakagawa, 'Magnetic Field Deficiency Syndrome and Magnetic Treatment', *Japan Med. Jnl.* 2745, Dec 4 (1976).

B. E. W. Nordenstrom, Cieszynski, Meyerson, 'Dc on kidney function; correcting child growth; development of ideas on EM field EFFS in humans, *Int. Symp. on Electrobiology and its therapeutic applics*, Stockholm (1986).

H. Oldfield & R. W. Coghill, *The Dark Side of the Brain*, Element Books, Dorset (1988).

R. C. Olney, 'The treatment of Viral Hepatitis with the Knott Technique of blood irradiation', *Am. Jnl. Surg.* 90 (No. 3) p.402 (1955).

M. G. Orgel & W. J. O'Brien, *et al.*, 'Pulsing electromagnetic field therapy in nerve regeneration: An experimental study in the cat', *Plast. Reconstr. Surg.* 73: pp.173–82 (1984).

Robert Ornstein & David Sobel, *The Healing Brain*, Simon & Schuster, N.Y. (1987).

John M. Ott, *Health & Light: the effects of Natural & Artificial Light on Man and other Livings*, Devin–Adair, Old Greenwich (1973).

J. A. Parish & K. F. Jaenicke, 'Action Spectrum For Phototherapy of Psoriasis', *Jnl. Investig. Dermatol.* 76: pp.359–362 (1981).

J. G. Parish, 'Early outbreaks of epidemic neuroasthenia', *Postgrad Med. Jnl.* 54: pp.711–7 (1978).

V. Ottani, *et al.*, 'Influence of pulsed electromagnetic fields on regenerating rat liver after partial hepatectomy', *J. Anat.* 139 pp.253–63 (1984).

M. A. Patterson, 'Treatment of drug, alcohol and nicotine addiction by neuroelectric therapy: Analysis of results over 7 years', *J. Bioelectricity* 3 (1&2): pp.193–221 (1984).

W. E. Penfield & E. Boldrey, 'Somatic and Sensory representation in the cerebral cortex of man as studied by electrical stimulation', *Brain* 60: pp.389–443 (1937).

Freiherr Gustav von Pohl, *Earth Currents – causative factor of cancer and other diseases*, Freich-verlag, Feucht (1983).

H. Pohl, 'Natural oscillating fields of cells', *Coherent excitations in biological systems*, Springer Verlag, pp.199–210 (1983).

Bruce Pomeranz, 'Effects of applied DC fields on sprouting and motor-nerve regeneration in adult rats', In *Ionic Currents in Development* (ed. R. Nutichelli) Liss, N.Y. (1985).

B. Pomeranz, M. Mullen and H. Markus, 'Effect of applied electrical fields on sprouting of intact saphenous nerve in adult rat,' *Brain Research 303*, (1984), pp.331–336, Elsevier.

A. Prusinski, *et al.*, 'Pulsating electromagnetic field in the theory of headache', *J. Bioelectricity* 7(1) pp.127–8 (1988).

J. R. Quinan, 'The use of the magnet in medicine: a historical study', *Maryland Med. Jnl.* 14 pp.460–5 (1886).

M. Reichmanis, *et al.*, 'Electrical correlates of acupuncture points', *IEEE Trans. Biomed. Eng.* BME 22 pp.533–5 (1975).

Martin Reite, *et al.*, 'Sleep Inducing Effects of Low-Energy Emission Therapy', *Abstracts: BEMS* 12th Annual Meeting, San Antonio, Texas (1990).

Russel J. Reiter, 'Effects of Light and stress on pineal function', *ELF EM Fields: the question of Cancer* (eds Wilson, Stevens *et al*), Battelle Press, Ohio (1990).

Oliver Sacks, 'Migraine: evolution of a common disorder', Faber and Faber, London (1970).

G. Salara, *et al.*, 'Effects of transcutaneous electrotherapy on CFS B-endorphin content in patients without pain problems', *Pain* 20 pp.169–72 (1981).

C. Salter, 'Quantifying skin disease and healing in vivo using electrical impedance measurements' In: *Non-Invasive Physiological Measurements* (ed. P. Rolfe), Academic Press, London 1:21-68 (1979).

D. C. Schecter, 'Origins of electrotherapy: Part I', *NY State J. Medicine:* 71 p.1002 (1971).

E. Schrodinger, 'What is life?', C.U.P. Cambridge (1944) (reprinted 1967).

N. A. Schultz, 'The effects of solar activity on the white blood count', Life in the Universe, Mysl. Moscow, p. 382 (1964).

National Academy of Science, 'Biological impacts of increased intensities of solar ultraviolet radiation', Washington (1973).

A. M. Scofield, 'Homeopathy and its potential role in agriculture – a critical review', *Prog. Agric Hortic* 2, 1-50 (1984).

Dr G. Laughton Scott, MRCS, LRCP, BA, 'The Abrams Treatment in Practice – an investigation', Geoffrey Bles, London (1924).

W. J. W. Sharrad, 'Treatment of congenital and infantile pseudarthrosis of the tibia with pulsing electromagnetic fields', *Orthop. Clin. North Am.* 15: 143-161 (1984).

G. H. Sidaway, 'Some Early Experiments in Electroculture', *Jnl. Electrostatics* 1: 389–393 (1975).

B. Sjound, *et al*, 'Increased cerebrospinal fluid levels of endorphins after electroacupuncture', *Acta Physiol. Scand.* 100: 382-384 (1977).

C. W. Smith & E. Aarholt, 'Possible effects of environmentally simulated endogenous opiates', *Health Physics* 43 (6): 929-930 (1982).

Cyril Smith & Simon Best, 'Electromagnetic Man', J.M. Dent, Clapham, U.K. (1989).

Cyril W. Smith, 'Clinical effects at high dilutions', *Volume of proceedings 42nd congress of the International Homoeopathic Medical League,* Pages 272-81.

K. C. Smith, 'The Science of Photobiology', Plenum Press, N.Y. (1977).

S. D. Smith, 'Limb regeneration', In: *Modern Bioelectricity* (ed. A. A. Marino); Marcel Dekker, New York, 529-55 (1988).

George F. Solomon & A. A. Amkraut, 'Immunity Emotions & Stress', *Annals, Emotions & Stress.*

Fred Soyka with Alan Edmonds, 'The Ion Effect', Bantam, Toronto & N.Y. (1978).

Jacob Stangle, 'Radiation measurements over underground aquifers (in German)', *Bohrtechnik Brunnenbau Rohrleitungsbau Nr. 11* (1960).

T. M. Stark & P. M. Sinclair, 'Effect of pulsing electromagnetic fields on orthodontic tooth movement', *Am. J. Orthod. Dentofacial Orthop.* 91: 91-104 (1987).

Jesse A. Stoff & Sheldon P. Stoff, 'Induced electrical changes at acupuncture points by homoeopathic remedies', *Alternative Med.* vol.2 Nos 3/4 pp.181–193 (1987).

F. G. Sulman, 'Influence of artificial air ionisation on the human EEG', *Int. Jnl. of Biometeriol.* 18 (1974).

F. G. Sulman, 'The effect of air Ionization, electric fields, atmospherics, and other electric phenomena on man and animal', C.C. Thomas, Springfield, Ill. (1980).

S. Takashima & R. Sukura, 'Desickling of sickled erythrocytes by pulsed r-f field', *Science* 220: pp.411-13, 21 April (1983).

Roger B. Taylor, P. H. Duffus *et al.*, 'Redistribution and pinocytosis of lymphocyte surface immunoglobulin molecules induced by anti-immunoglobulin antibody', *Nature New Biol.* 232: pp.225–29 (1971).

T. S. Tenforde, 'Electroreception and Magnetoreception in simple and complex Organisms', *BEMS* 10 (3) pp. 215-221 (1989).

Peter Tomkins & Christopher Bird, 'The Secret Life of Plants', Allen Lane, London (1974).

Pamela Trauger, 'Detection of body's ambient radiation may produce truly noninvasive imaging,' *Radiology Today*, p.4 & 7, Vol. 6, August (1989).

P. A. Valberg & A. A. Feldman, 'Magnetic particle motions within living cells', *BioPhys. Jnl.* 52: pp.551-561 (1987).

N. V. Vasile & E. V. Vasile, 'Effect of constant and alternating magnetic fields on the immunobiological response of the organism,' *Question of Haematology Radiobiology with the Biological action of magnetic fields*, Tomsk p.379 (1965).

R. Virchow, 'Cellular pathology', Classics of Medicine Library, Gryphond Editions, Alabama (1860. reprint 1978).

O. Wahlstrom, 'Electromagnetic fields used in the treatment of fresh fractures of the radius', *2nd Ann. BRAGS*, Oxford, p.26 (1982).

B. Watson, 'Medical Electronics & Physics at Bart's, 1964–1986', London Dept of Med. Electronics, St Bartholomew's Hospital (1986).

J. D. Watson & F. H. C. Crick, 'Molecular structure of nucleic acids: a structure for deoxyribonucleic acid,' *Nature* 171: pp.737–738 (1953).

Lyall Watson, 'The Biology of Death (prev. The Romeo Error)',

Sceptre Books (Hodder & Stoughton) (1974 rev. 1987).

J. C. Weaver & Alan Barnett, 'Weak Electromagnetic Field Effects: Possible Interaction Mechanisms', Abstracts: BEMS 12th Annual Meeting, San Antonio, Texas (1990).

S. J. Webb, 'Genetic continuity and metabolic regulation as seen by the effects of various microwave and black light frequencies on these phenomena', *Ann. NY. Acad. Sci.* 247: pp.327-351 (1975).

S. J. Webb, 'Synthesis of DNA by specific frequencies', *Ann. NY. Acad. Sci.* 247: pp.327 (1975).

S. J. Webb, 'Turning cancer cells to normal with microwaves,' *Int. Jnl. of Quant Chem Quant Biol.* 1 Symp. 1, pp.245-251.

S. J. Webb, 'Newly dev. approaches to disease: the crystal properties of living cells, their control over normal cell activities and role in oncogenic and virally-induced malfunctions', *IRCS Med. J.* 14, p.98 (1986).

S. Weisburd, 'DNA helix found to oscillate in resonance with microwaves,' *Science News* Vol. 12.

P. Weiss, 'Interactions between cells,' *Rev. Mod. Phys.* 31: p.449 (1959b).

Paul Weiss, 'Principles of Development,' Holt, NY (1939).

H. L. Wen & S. Y. Cheng, 'Treatment of drug addiction by acupuncture and electrical stimulation', *Asian J. Med.* 9: pp. 138-41 (1973).

H. L. Wen & S. Y. C. Cheng, 'Treatment of drug addiction by acupuncture and electrical stimulation', *Amer. J. Acupuncture* 1: pp. 71-5 (1973).

H. V. Westerhoff, T. W. Tsong *et al*, 'How enzymes can capture and transmit free energy from an oscillating electric field', *Proc. Natl. Acad. Sci. USA.* 83: pp4734-4738 (1986).

Aubrey Westlake, 'The Pattern of Health: a search for a greater understanding of the life force in health and disease', Devin-Adair, NY (1961).

J. Wigglesworth, 'On the use of galvanism in the treatment of certain forms of insanity,' *BMJ.* II: 506-507 (1987).

E. P. Wigner, 'Every phenomenon is unexpected and most unlikely until it has been discovered – and some of them remain unreasonable for a long time after they have been discovered,' *Symmetries and reflections* MIT Press Camb. USA, 1987.

W. Wiktor-Jedrzejczak, A. Ahmed, *et al*. 'Immune response of mice to 2450 MHz microwave radiation: Overview of immunology and empiric studies of lymphoid splenic cells.' *Radio Sci.* 12: pp209-218 (1977).

A. Wildervanck, K. G. Wakim *et al.* 'Certain experimental observations on a pulsed diathermy machine,' *Arch. Physics Med. & Rehab.* 40: pp.45-55 (1959).

Marcia Wilkinson, 'Migraine and Headaches,' Martin Dunitz, London (1982).

T. Williamson, 'Dowsing adheres new credence,' *New Scientist* 81, pp.381-3 (1979).

B. Wilson, 'Chronic Exposure to ELF fields can induce depression,' *Bioelectromagnetics.* Vol. 9: pp.195-205 (1988).

Mark A. Wilson, 'Extremely Low Frequency Electromagnetic Field Effects On Short Term Memory,' Abstracts: BEMS 12th Annual Meeting, San Antonio, Texas (1990).

Arthur T. Winfree, 'Human body clocks and the timing of sleep,' *Nature,* 297: pp.23-27, 6 May (1982).

I. G. N. Rody Wirya, 'Bioquantum Mechanical Theory of the Mechanism of Acupuncture and Related Modalities,' *Amer. Jnl. of Acupuncture,* p.235-, Vol. 16, No 3, July-September (1988).

C. N. Woolsey, 'Patterns of sensory representation in the cerebral cortex,' *Fed. Proc. Amer. Soc. Exp. Biol.* 6: pp.437-441 (1947).

Valerie Worwood, 'Aromantics', Pan Books, London (1987).

M. F. Zanakis & M. J. Politis, 'Partial recovery from spinal cord injury following application of DC electric fields in the rat: Paper presented at the 18th Annual Meeting of the Society for Neuroscience, Nov. 13-18, 1988, Toronto, Ontario,' *Society for Neuroscience Abstracts,* 14: p.496 (1988).

Index